AGS

# Exploring American
# HISTORY

by
Penny Konlyn

AGS®
American Guidance Service, Inc.
4201 Woodland Road
Circle Pines, MN 55014-1796
1-800-328-2560

## Learning About Our United States

**Cover photo credit:** Images © 1996 Photo Disc, Inc.



Printed in the United States of America

ISBN 0–7854–0960–2 (Previously ISBN 0–88671–468–0)

Order Number: 90871

A 0 9 8 7 6 5

# Contents

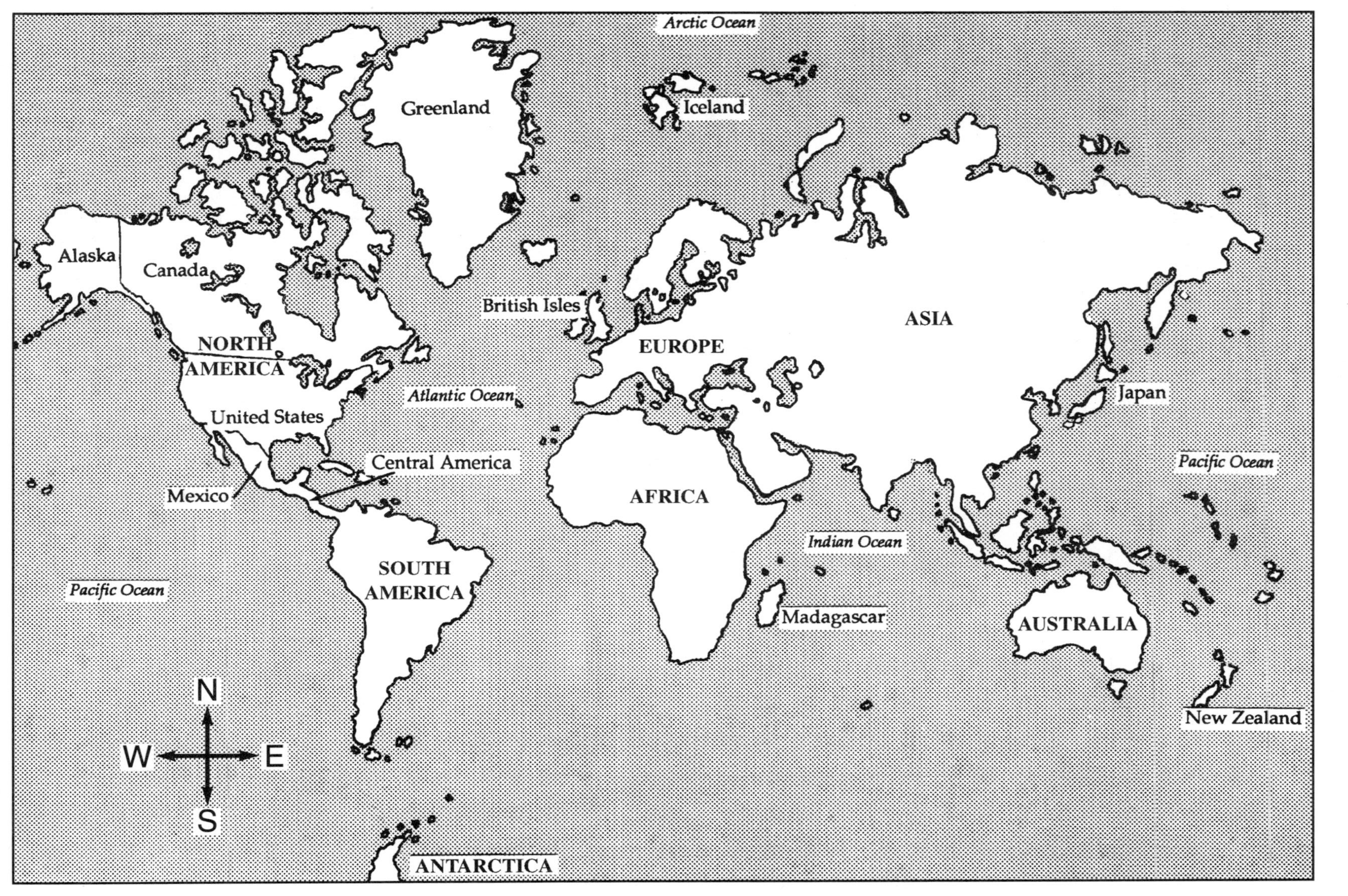


A Map of the World

# The United States and the World

Lesson 1

UNIT 1

Before you can begin learning about United States history, you must know where to find your country on a world map. You must also learn where other countries are because they are a part of United States history, too.

Look at the globe in your classroom. This globe shows you what the earth looks like. Notice the picture of the globe on this page. You can also look at a flat map of the world.

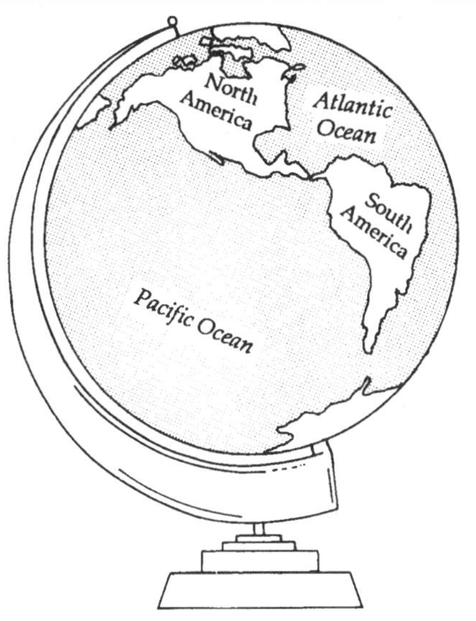


**Global Views of the World**

### What Did You Find Out?

**A** Look at the map on page 4. Use it to complete these exercises.

1. Color all water on your map blue. Color all land on your map brown. The world is made up of

   ____________________ (blue) and ____________________ (brown).

2. The world map shows you that there are some large pieces of land. Some of these large pieces of land are called *continents.* Each continent's name is shown in all capital letters. Write the continents' names.

   a. ____________________ e. ____________________

   b. ____________________ f. ____________________

   c. ____________________ g. ____________________

   d. ____________________

3. The world map shows you that there are four large bodies of water. A large body of water is called an *ocean.* Each ocean has a name. Write the names of the oceans.

   a. ____________________ c. ____________________

   b. ____________________ d. ____________________

4. Find the United States on the world map. With the exception of Hawaii, all of the United States is on the continent of ____________________.

5. Use the direction finder, or compass rose, on the map to answer the following:

   a. Put your finger on the United States on the world map. Look at the compass rose. The N on the rose stands for *north.* Point north of the United States on the map. What country is directly north of the United States?

   ____________________

UNIT 1

**b.** Look at the compass rose. South is the opposite direction of north. Point your finger south on the map. What country is on the southern border of the United States?

______________________

**c.** Look at the compass rose. The E on the rose stands for *east.* Point to the east on the map. What ocean is east of the United States?

______________________

**d.** West is the opposite direction of east. Point your finger to the west on the map. What ocean is west of the United States?

______________________

**B** Fill in the missing words in the puzzle below. The letters in the shaded areas will spell the name of the map on page 4.

1. The opposite of east is ____.
2. The continent that is west of Europe is ____ America.
3. The continent that is north of Africa is ____.
4. The ____ Ocean is east of North America.
5. The country that is north of the United States is ____.

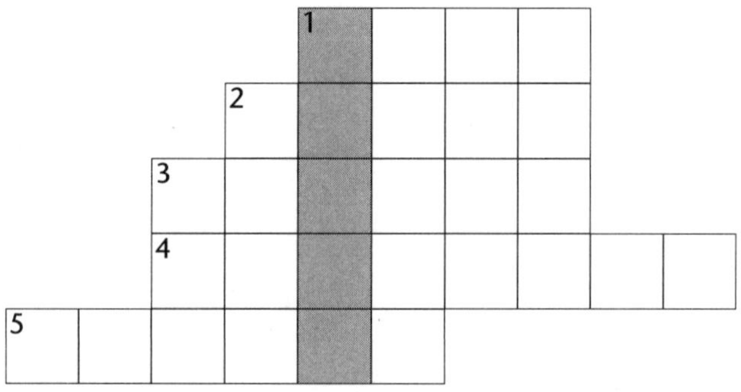


What does the map on page 4 show?

__________________________________

**C** Match the following words in column 1 with their meanings in column 2.

| | | |
|---|---|---|
| ______ | 1. continents | a. seven large landmasses |
| ______ | 2. globe | b. country north of the United States |
| ______ | 3. Pacific Ocean | c. the round model that represents the earth |
| ______ | 4. Canada | d. to the west of the United States |

# The First Americans



The history of our country begins with the first people who lived in North America. The first people may have come to the Americas by crossing a land bridge from Asia to Alaska that formed during the last ice age. They were hunters following herds of large animals. Over time, people spread throughout North and South America. These first Americans were the ancestors of the American Indians.

Many different groups of Indians lived in the Americas. They developed rich and varied cultures. Their ways of life were suited to the environments in which they lived. They used the resources of the land to meet their needs for food, clothing, and shelter. For example, the Northwest Coast Indians lived near the Pacific Ocean in an area with huge forests. The ocean offered plenty of seafood, and the forests had many large animals such as moose and bear that the people hunted. The forests provided wood that the Indians used to build their houses and canoes. They also made wooden boxes, utensils, and masks.

Many Indians in North America lived in groups called *tribes.* Tribes were made up of many families. All members of a tribe spoke the same language and had the same religion, customs, and way of life. Each tribe had at least one leader, often called *chief.*

Scientists and historians have identified a number of American Indian culture areas. For example, the Northeast culture area includes people living in areas from the present-day Canadian border to the Ohio Valley and from the Atlantic Coast to about the Mississippi River. For the most part, Indian tribes living in this culture area farmed, hunted, and gathered. Most lived in villages, and their houses were made to protect the people from the cold winters. The Iroquois, for example, built large houses, called *long houses,* that had sections for individual families.

Indians moved from one place to another on foot or in boats called *canoes.* Canoes were made from hollowed-out trees, bark, or animal skins. Some were large and heavy, while others were very light. Most Indians who used canoes lived in the eastern part of our country or on the Pacific Coast.

For many years only Indians lived on this continent. Then European settlers came. The arrival of the Europeans resulted in many changes in the Americas, Europe, and Africa. A great exchange of resources began. The Europeans brought to the Americas horses, sheep, cattle, chickens, wheat, and sugar among other resources. They took home such goods as corn, tomatoes, potatoes, squash, tobacco, chocolate, peanuts, and pineapples. Unfortunately, the Europeans also brought diseases unknown in the Americas. Indians had no immunity to, or ability to fight, these diseases. As a result, millions died of smallpox, cholera, and other diseases.

UNIT 1

Indians and Europeans had different views about the use and ownership of land. To the settlers, land represented great wealth. Settlers often took over Indian lands. The Indians did not want to give up their lands. This land dispute and other issues led to fighting. Many Indians and settlers were killed in the fighting.

Settlers eventually took over most Indian lands. Later, some areas were set aside for Indian use. These areas of land were called *reservations.* The Indians were also promised food and other kinds of help if they moved to the reservations. There, they had to give up their old ways of living.

As time went by, many Indians were forced to change their ways of living. Some became cattle or sheep raisers. Since most reservations did not have good farmland, very few became farmers. Many rented their lands to settlers.

Today there are about two million Indians in our country. Most do not live on reservations. Many Indians maintain some of their old skills, arts, and traditions. Many of these skills—pottery and basket weaving, beading, and quill work—have been passed down from one generation to the next.

Challenges still face Indians today. About one-third live on reservations, and many live in poverty. Unemployment is very high, and life expectancy low. Like all people, Indians want to improve the quality of their lives. Many are working to achieve that goal.

**American History Time Line**
Turn to the American History Time Line on page 93. On line 1, write "Indians are the only people in North America."

**What Did You Find Out?**

**A** Look at the map on page 9. Then answer the questions.

1. Which Indians lived in hogans? ______________________
2. In what area of the country will you find the Hopi pueblos? ______________________
3. What tribe built long houses? ______________________
4. Which tribe lived in domed bark lodges? ______________________
5. From what did the Sioux make their tepees? ______________________

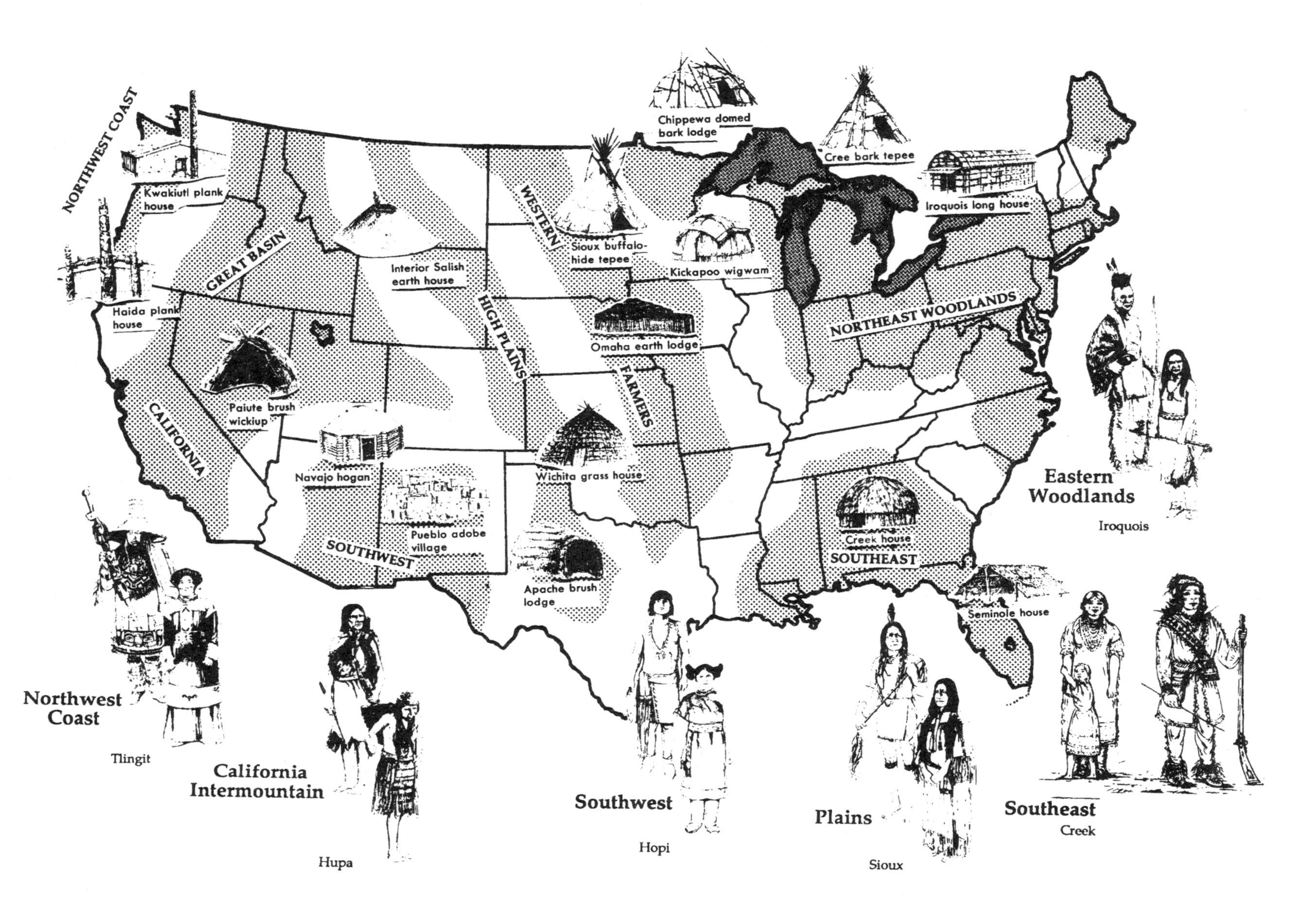


**Clothing and Homes Used by Major American Indian Tribes in the United States**

UNIT 1

**B** Write the word or words that best answer the following questions.

1. What was the leader of a tribe often called? ______________________
2. Where might the first people in the Americas have come from? ______________________
3. What was the main thing Europeans took from the Indians? ______________________
4. What were the land areas called that were set aside for Indian use? ______________________
5. About how many Indians live in the United States today? ______________________
6. What is the name given to the boats used by some Indians? ______________________
7. Name three European resources brought to the Americas. Name three American resources taken to Europe.

______________________________________________

______________________________________________

**C** Underline the word that best completes each of the following sentences.

1. The ancestors of the Indians probably came to the Americas from (Europe, Africa, Asia).
2. Indians used their resources for food, shelter, and (fun, explorers, clothing).
3. The Indians and settlers mainly fought each other over (land, gold and silver, canoes).
4. Canoes were made from hollowed-out trees, animal skins, or (steel, wooden planks, bark).
5. On the reservations, many Indians became (farmers, sheep and cattle raisers, hunters).

**D** Many words that you know come from Indian words. Match the clues in the second column to the words from Indian languages in the first column.

| | | |
|---|---|---|
| _____ | 1. moccasin | a. a deerlike animal with big antlers |
| _____ | 2. Chicago | b. beans and sweet corn mixed together |
| _____ | 3. moose | c. the name of a small state |
| _____ | 4. succotash | d. the largest city in Illinois |
| _____ | 5. Mississippi | e. the name of a soft shoe; also, a snake |
| _____ | 6. Connecticut | f. a large river in the United States; also, the name of a state |

# The First European Explorers

Lesson 3

UNIT 1

In Lesson 2, you learned what North America was like before the European explorers came. An explorer is a person who investigates places or ideas unfamiliar to him or her.

The European explorers who first came to North America were looking for trade routes to the Indies, the name they gave to India, China, Japan, and other nations of Asia. For a long time, the Europeans had been buying goods, such as spices, silk, and gems, from Arabian traders who brought the goods from the Indies. The Europeans wanted to trade with the Indies directly, and so they began looking for routes that would take them directly to the Indies.

These explorers faced many challenges. They made very long trips, called *voyages,* over the ocean. Their wooden ships were very small. There was little room on them for supplies. The crew members on these ships often got sick. Many died because there was not enough nutritious food, water, or medicine.

Most of the explorers sailed for the European countries of Spain and Portugal. At that time in history, Europeans did not know that the western continents of North America and South America even existed! Their maps showed only the eastern continents of Europe, Asia, and Africa.

One of the best-known European explorers was Christopher Columbus. He sailed west with three ships from Spain in 1492. He was looking for a short route to the Indies. Columbus did not know about the continents of North and South America. When he landed on islands near North and South America, he thought he had reached the Indies.

Later other nations, such as France, England, and the Netherlands, sent explorers to the Americas. They tried to find a route around the Americas to the Indies. They also explored the lands of North and South America.

Look at the map on page 12. Find Spain. Trace the route that Columbus took in 1492 from Spain to the Americas in red.

**A Ship of the Early Explorers**

UNIT 1

John Cabot sailed from England. He explored the eastern coast of North America. Look at your map again. Find England. Trace Cabot's route in green.

Another famous explorer was Ferdinand Magellan. Magellan sailed from Spain. He was looking for a southern route around the Americas that would lead to India. Although Magellan died before the voyage was over, his crew succeeded in sailing around the world.

Look at your map again. With your finger, follow the line that shows part of Magellan's voyage as his crew sailed from Spain and then returned there. Trace the route in blue.

There were many other Europeans who explored the Americas. Little by little, they explored and claimed for their countries more and more of the Americas.

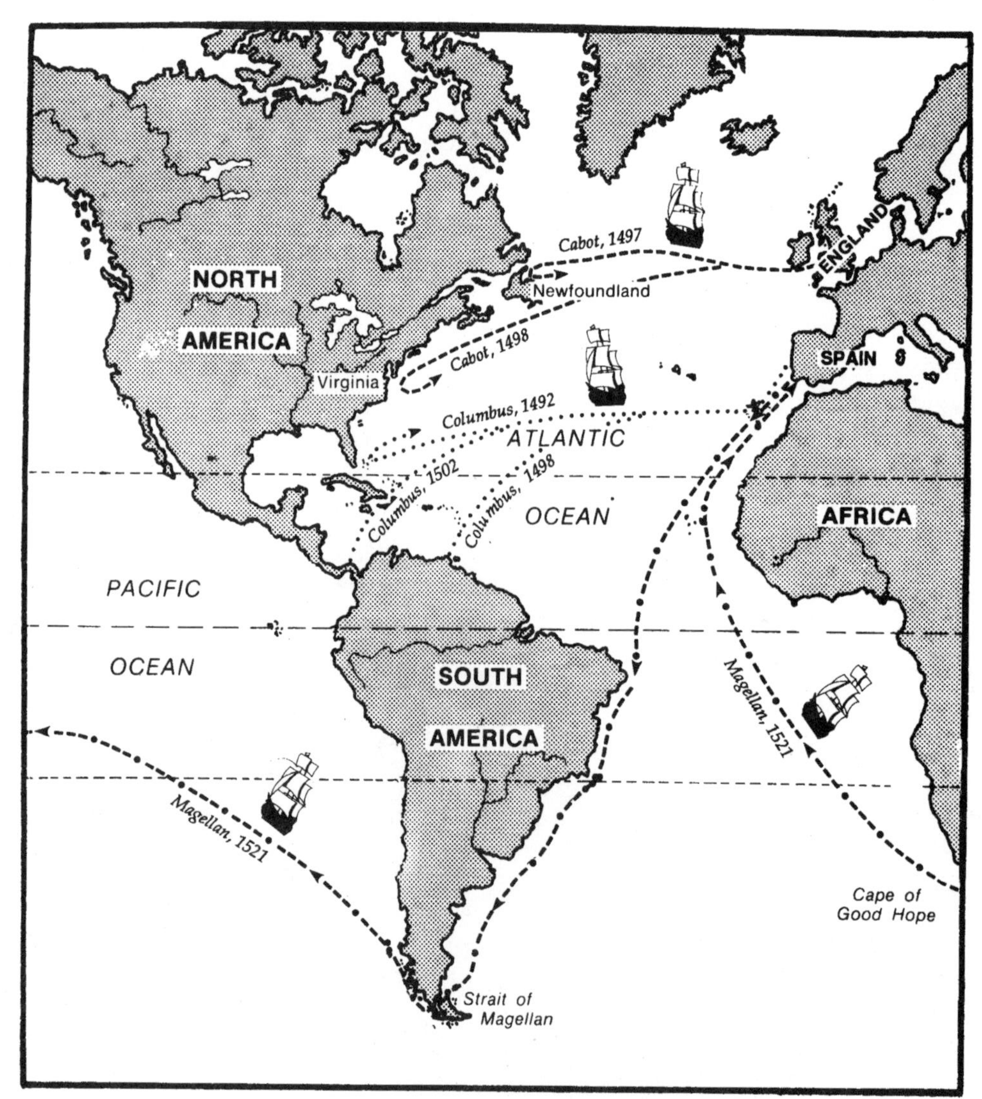


**The Routes of Columbus, Cabot, and Magellan**

**American History Time Line**
Turn to the American History Time Line on page 93. On line 2, write "Europeans explore the Americas."

## What Did You Find Out?

**A** Write *True* or *False* on the line before each statement.

_______________ **1.** Most of the explorers came from North America.

_______________ **2.** In 1492, Columbus sailed from Spain.

_______________ **3.** Magellan's crew became the first to sail completely around the world.

_______________ **4.** England did not support any exploration of the Americas.

_______________ **5.** A voyage is a long trip by water.

**B** Complete the sentences by matching the subject in column 1 with the best ending in column 2.

| | Column 1 | Column 2 |
|---|---|---|
| ________ | **1.** The Indies | **a.** sailed west from Spain in search of the Indies. |
| ________ | **2.** Magellan | **b.** sailed from England. |
| ________ | **3.** An explorer | **c.** was the European name for the countries of Asia. |
| ________ | **4.** John Cabot | **d.** is a person who investigates unfamiliar lands or ideas. |
| ________ | **5.** Columbus | **e.** died, but his crew sailed around the world. |

**C** Fill in the missing words in the sentences below.

**1.** The two western continents that the Europeans did not know about were ____________________ and ____________________.

**2.** The three eastern continents that the Europeans knew about were ____________________, ____________________, and ____________________.

**D** Put these sentences in the correct order by writing 1, 2, 3, or 4 on the lines provided.

_____ Europeans explore American lands.

_____ Hunters may have crossed a land bridge joining Asia and the Americas.

_____ Only Indians live in North America.

_____ Columbus sails west in hopes of finding a route to the Indies.

UNIT 1

**E** Complete the puzzle. Choose answers from the word list below.

**Word List**
Cabot
Columbus
England
explorers
Indies
Magellan
Spain
spice
trade

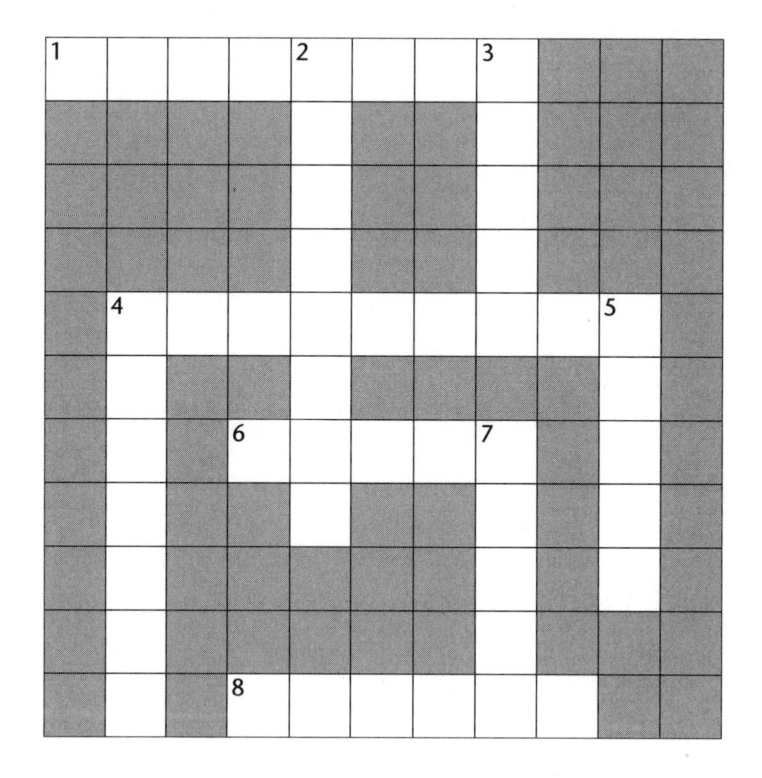


**Across**

1. This was a European explorer who reached the Americas in 1492.
4. These people investigate new places or ideas.
6. This explorer sailed along the eastern coast of North America.
8. This was the European name for China, India, and other countries of Asia.

**Down**

2. This explorer's crew sailed around the world.
3. This is one of the Asian goods Europeans wanted.
4. John Cabot sailed for this country.
5. Explorers from this country sailed around the world.
7. European explorers were looking for this kind of route to Asia.

# The First Settlers



The first European explorers claimed the American lands for their countries. These countries sent more explorers to the Americas. They were looking for riches such as silver and gold. They were looking for places to live.

Many people who lived in Europe wanted to come to North America. These people had many reasons for leaving their homes and friends. Some wanted to be free to worship, or pray, as they pleased. Some wanted to teach their religion to the Indians. Others did not like the way their countries were ruled. Some people hoped to find gold and other riches. Almost everyone who came to North America was looking for a better life.

**A Pilgrim**

Soon hundreds and hundreds of people sailed from Europe to North America. The French had settlers in what is now Canada and the middle of the United States. Spain had colonies in southern North America and South America. England had colonies on the eastern seacoast of what is now the United States.

When the English came here, they built small houses and formed settlements. Most of the settlements were established in colonies. A colony is a larger group of people who joined together for common goals. In all, thirteen colonies made up England's claim in North America.

The first successful English settlement in North America was Jamestown, established in 1607. At first, life in the colony was very hard. Many of the people in Jamestown did not use their time wisely. Some of them spent time looking for gold instead of planting crops. When winter came, many of these settlers died because there was not enough food.

A few years later, another group of people left England and sailed to North America. These people landed at Plymouth, Massachusetts, in 1620. Today, we call them the Pilgrims. During their first winter in America, many Pilgrims died from hunger and cold.

The Pilgrims and Indians became friends. The Indians showed the Pilgrims how to plant corn. After the first harvest, they had a big celebration together. The Pilgrims gave thanks for their new land and new friendships with the Indians.

This was one of the first American thanksgivings. Today, in November, Americans celebrate Thanksgiving. They give thanks for the freedom and opportunities that the United States provides.

Before long, more people from Europe began to arrive in the thirteen colonies. People came from many countries: Sweden, the Netherlands, Germany, and Ireland. Gradually, many settlers moved westward to unsettled land. They found

UNIT 1

good farming land with many rivers that provided water and excellent transportation. Farming, lumbering, and fur trapping became important work for the people who settled on these lands.

Life changed in the American colonies. Towns and cities grew in number and size. Colonial trade and industries provided jobs and opportunities. A spirit of independence was growing. The desire for freedom from British control would soon bring about an important event in the history of America.

**American History Time Line**
Turn to the American History Time Line on page 93. On line 3, write "England establishes colonies in North America."

### What Did You Find Out?

**A** Underline the word that best completes each statement.

1. The European country that set up colonies on the eastern coast of what is now the United States was (Russia, Portugal, England).
2. North America is in the (Western Hemisphere, Eastern Hemisphere, Southern Hemisphere).
3. All the people who came from Europe to live in North America were known as (Indians, settlers, Pilgrims).
4. Jamestown was settled by people from (England, Spain, France).
5. A special day that reminds us of the Pilgrims is (Memorial Day, Thanksgiving Day, Flag Day).
6. There were (five, eight, thirteen) English colonies in North America.

**B** Write the words that go with the descriptions.

1. The name of the first Americans ____________________
2. The name of one explorer ____________________
3. The name of one English colony ____________________
4. A large landmass ____________________
5. A large body of water ____________________
6. The name of our country ____________________
7. The number of English colonies in North America ____________________
8. A long trip by water ____________________

**C** The people in Europe had many reasons for coming to the Americas. List four reasons on the lines below.

Reason 1: ______________________

Reason 2: ______________________

Reason 3: ______________________

Reason 4: ______________________

**D** Use a dictionary to find the meanings of the following words.

1. colony ______________________
2. settler ______________________
3. worship ______________________
4. freedom ______________________

**E** Read the words listed in the box below. Choose the word that will complete each of the following sentences. Write your answers on the lines.

| | | | |
|---|---|---|---|
| independence | British | trade | Plymouth |
| settlers | rivers | westward | Jamestown |

1. Groups of ______________ joined together to form a colony.
2. ______________ was the first successful English colony in North America.
3. The Pilgrims landed at ______________ in 1620.
4. Settlers went ______________ in search of good farmland.
5. The region had many good ______________ for water and transportation.
6. All through the colonies, a spirit of ______________ was growing.
7. Colonial ______________ and industries provided opportunities.
8. The desire for freedom from ______________ control would soon bring about an important event in our history.

## Using a Map

The map below shows the eastern coast of the continent of North America. Thirteen colonies were set up in North America by England.

Fill in the name of each colony. The Word List will help you.

**Word List**
- Connecticut
- Delaware
- Georgia
- Maryland
- Massachusetts
- New Hampshire
- New Jersey
- New York
- North Carolina
- Pennsylvania
- Rhode Island
- South Carolina
- Virginia

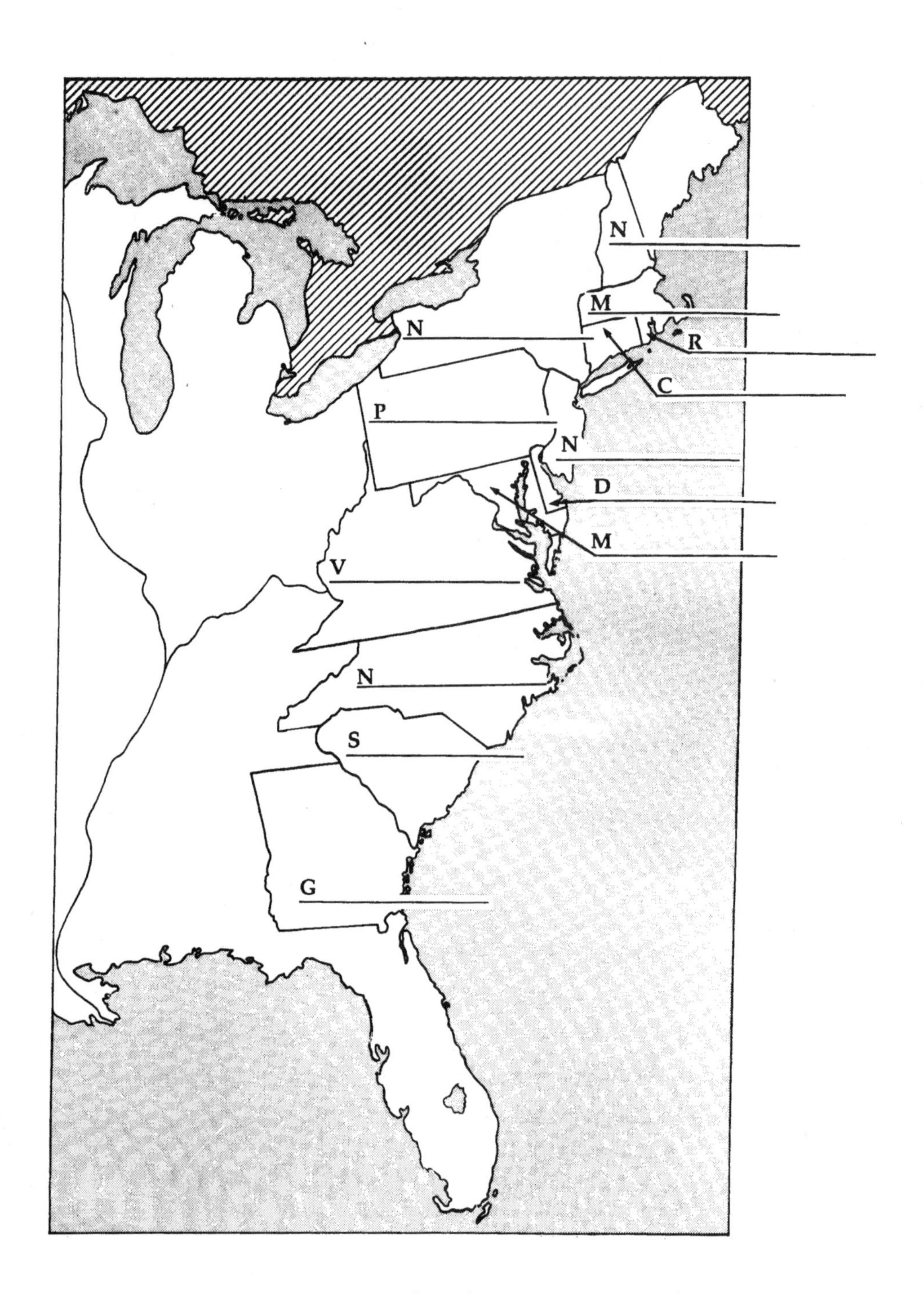


**The Thirteen Colonies**

# The Colonies and Great Britain



At first, life was hard for settlers in the English, or British, colonies. As time went on, however, life became easier. The colonists cleared the land, built towns and cities, and slowly made progress. The settlers had enough lumber and furs to send some to the people in England. In return, they got many of the items they needed from England. This was called *trading.* This growing trade helped both England and the colonies become richer.

**King George III**

For years, Britain allowed the colonies to govern themselves in many matters. During this time, Britain was occupied in fighting a number of wars with other countries. One of these wars, called the *French and Indian War* in America, started in the 1750s. Britain and France were fighting over who would control the land west of the thirteen colonies. Britain eventually won the war, and France lost its North American lands as a result.

After the war, troubles rapidly developed between Britain and its American colonies. Help was needed to pay for the cost of the wars and also for protecting the settlers. King George III decided to place a series of taxes on the American colonies to raise the much needed money. He passed stricter trade laws. He wanted the colonists to pay more taxes on the items they got from Britain. The king also began taking a more active role in colonial affairs. He issued a declaration that limited the areas open to settlers. For these and other reasons, the colonies and Britain began to quarrel.

The new strict laws and taxes caused trouble in the colonies. King George III tried to make the thirteen colonies obey his laws by sending many more soldiers to the colonies. In 1770, some British soldiers fired their rifles into a crowd of colonists who were protesting in Boston, Massachusetts. Five colonists were killed. Among those killed was Crispus Attucks, an African American who had escaped slavery many years earlier. This incident was called the *Boston Massacre.*

The "Boston Tea Party" of 1773 was the reaction of colonists in Boston to a tax on tea. Led by Samuel Adams and John Hancock, colonists dressed up as Indians and dumped chests of tea into Boston Harbor. The king was very angry and closed the harbor. He was determined to make the colonists obey his laws.

In 1774, the First Continental Congress met in Philadelphia. The members, or *delegates,* decided to write a Declaration of Rights that they would send to the king. The delegates made it very clear in their declaration that they felt the British had no right to tax the colonists. They said that because they were not represented in the British Parliament, the Parliament had no right to tax them.

The declaration only made the king more unhappy with the colonists. Instead of changing the laws, he demanded that the laws be enforced. The colonists prepared to take more steps. A second meeting was planned for the following year.

In 1775, the Second Continental Congress met in Philadelphia. Another document was sent to the king. This document stated that changes had to be made. Again, the king was very angry and closed the colonies to trade, saying they were in a state of rebellion.

The problems between England and the American colonies lasted over a decade. Some of the colonists sided with England. However, many others became dissatisfied with their treatment by George III. They wanted a more active say in the decisions that affected the colonies in America. The British government was mostly unwilling to give them this right.

Over this period of time, the British colonists had begun to think of themselves as Americans first and as British second. The time had come for them to make a great decision. Should they fight for freedom or obey the king?

### What Did You Find Out?

**A** Identify the following names and words. Explain how they are important in the history of the thirteen colonies.

1. original colonies ____________________
2. British ____________________
3. taxes ____________________
4. King George III ____________________
5. Samuel Adams ____________________
6. Philadelphia ____________________
7. Declaration of Rights ____________________
8. Continental Congress ____________________
9. Boston Massacre ____________________
10. Boston Tea Party ____________________

**B** Underline the word or words that best complete each statement.

1. The French and Indian War was fought between (the French and the Indians, the French and the English, the English and the colonists).
2. The King of England thought that the colonists should pay (no taxes, more taxes, very few taxes).
3. Among those killed at the Boston Massacre was (Samuel Adams, John Hancock, Crispus Attucks).
4. The Boston Tea Party took place in the year (1773, 1753, 1763).
5. One of the organizers of the Boston Tea Party was (Crispus Attucks, King George III, Samuel Adams).
6. The Boston Tea Party took place at the (First Continental Congress, Boston harbor, Parliament).
7. The First Continental Congress met in the city of (Jamestown, Philadelphia, Boston).
8. The members of the First Continental Congress were called (soldiers, delegates, settlers).
9. (Some, All, None) of the colonists wanted to obey the king.
10. The Declaration of Rights was sent to the king by the (First Continental Congress, Second Continental Congress, Boston Tea Party).
11. The French and Indian War resulted in (England, Spain, France) losing its North American territory.

**C** Answer each of the following questions. Use complete sentences.

1. Why did King George III need more money?

______________________________________________

______________________________________________

2. What did the king do to raise money in America?

______________________________________________

______________________________________________

3. What was the Declaration of Rights?

______________________________________________

______________________________________________

______________________________________________

# The Revolutionary War



The first real fighting between the Americans and the British took place in April 1775. General Thomas Gage, a British officer, ordered troops to march to Lexington and Concord. They were to capture military supplies that the Americans had stored at Concord. Gage may have intended for the troops to capture Samuel Adams and John Hancock, too. Paul Revere made his famous ride to warn the colonists. "The British are coming! The British are coming," he shouted. Fighting took place. Many British soldiers were killed, but only a few Americans. The war known as the American Revolution had begun.

**A Revolutionary War Soldier**

In 1776, delegates at the Second Continental Congress decided to tell the world that they wanted to be free from British rule. Their Declaration of Independence was approved on July 4. That date is our country's birthday. The Declaration of Independence was mostly written by Thomas Jefferson.

The fighting in the American Revolution lasted from 1775 to 1781. The Americans chose George Washington to be their commander in chief. At first, the Revolutionary War did not go very well for the Americans. General George Washington needed a big victory to boost the spirit of the American soldiers. The Battle of Saratoga, New York, was the turning point of the war. The Americans captured the whole army of British General John Burgoyne. After the great victory at Saratoga, France decided to help the Americans fight against the British. France had a very strong navy and would also send much needed supplies to the Americans. Some French soldiers, such as the Marquis de Lafayette, also helped the Americans in the Revolutionary War.

The battles in the American Revolution began in the New England colonies, moved to the middle colonies, and finally ended in the southern colonies. Other battles took place at sea, west of the settled land, and in the Middle West.

The fighting in the American Revolution did not come to an end until 1781. Lord Charles Cornwallis, a British general, marched his army to Yorktown, Virginia. Washington moved his large army southward from New York. The French navy blocked Chesapeake Bay. Cornwallis was trapped. He had no way to leave or to retreat. On October 19, 1781, Cornwallis surrendered his entire army. Two years later in 1783, the peace treaty was written in Paris, France. This treaty between the united colonies and England ended the American Revolution.

However, not all Americans were in favor of forming a new and separate country. Some Americans chose to leave the new United States and to move to Canada. Other Americans who remained loyal to England were forced to leave their homes and farms and to move to Canada or England. Most of the Americans who remained saw great benefits in being able to rule themselves. The colonies had become independent of England and a free nation, the United States of America.

**Famous Americans**

This famous American was a lawyer who worked for our country in many ways. He was elected to the legislature of Virginia. He served as the first secretary of state and was elected as the second Vice President. He was later elected President two times. When he was President, he made our country much larger by buying the Louisiana Territory from France. His home in Monticello, Virginia, is visited by many people today.

You know him in part because he wrote a very famous document that included these words: "We hold these truths to be self-evident, that all men are created equal." The document is called the *Declaration of Independence.*

Who is this famous American? Write his name on the line under his picture.

______________________________

UNIT 2

**American History Time Line**
Turn to the American History Time Line on page 93. On line 4, write "The colonies become independent."

## What Did You Find Out?

**A** Complete each of the following sentences. Write your answers on the lines provided.

1. The colonists decided to declare their independence from the king of ______________________.
2. This declaration is called the ______________________.
3. ______________________ wrote most of this declaration.
4. The Declaration of Independence was approved on ______________________.
5. ______________________ and ______________________ were the two cities in which fighting first took place.
6. The ______________________ War is the name given to the fighting between the Americans and the British.
7. Fighting first took place in the ______________________ colonies, then spread to the ______________________ colonies, and finally ended in the southern colonies.
8. The Revolutionary War lasted from ______________________ to ______________________.
9. The country of ______________________ sent soldiers and ships to help the Americans fight Britain.
10. The Battle of ______________________ was the turning point of the war.
11. Fighting ended in the year ______________________ when Lord Cornwallis surrendered.
12. The Americans won a great victory at ______________________, Virginia.
13. A peace treaty was written in the year ______________________.
14. The colonists won their freedom from ______________________ at the end of the Revolutionary War.

15. The American colonies became known as the ____________________ of America.

16. Some Americans chose to move to the country of ____________________ after the Revolutionary War.

**B** Each of the people listed in the box played an important role in the American Revolution. Choose the name that matches each description. Write these names on the lines provided.

| |
|---|
| Samuel Adams |
| Crispus Attucks |
| General Thomas Gage |
| General John Burgoyne |
| George III |
| George Washington |
| John Hancock |
| Lord Charles Cornwallis |
| Marquis de Lafayette |
| Paul Revere |

**Fighting in the Revolutionary War**

1. King of England ____________________
2. African American killed in the Boston Massacre ____________________
3. British officer who ordered his troops to march to Lexington and Concord ____________________
4. Colonist who made a famous ride to warn others that the British were coming ____________________
5. Commander of the American army ____________________
6. British general who surrendered his army at Yorktown ____________________
7. Two colonial leaders whom the British wanted to capture ____________________
8. British general who lost the Battle of Saratoga ____________________
9. French soldier who helped the Americans during the war ____________________

UNIT 2

**C** Put these sentences in the correct order by writing 1, 2, 3, 4, etc., on the lines provided.

_____ English colonists settle in Jamestown.

_____ Europeans explore the Americas.

_____ The French and Indian War ends.

_____ The colonies become a free country.

_____ The Revolutionary War begins.

_____ Only Indians live in North America.

**D** Answer each of the questions below in a complete sentence. Use your own words.

1. Why did Britain have little time to devote to the American colonies until after the French and Indian War?

______________________________________________________________________

______________________________________________________________________

2. The word *revolutionary* means "change." What were the changes the colonists wanted that led to the Revolutionary War?

______________________________________________________________________

______________________________________________________________________

3. Describe the ways in which France helped the American colonies during the Revolutionary War.

______________________________________________________________________

______________________________________________________________________

4. Why did Cornwallis surrender at Yorktown?______________________________

______________________________________________________________________

5. Why did some Americans decide to leave the new United States? ______________

______________________________________________________________________

# The Colonies Become a Country





The Revolutionary War was over. The Treaty of Paris was signed in 1783. The British recognized Americans' independence. The United States of America included all of the land westward to the Mississippi River. However, the British still controlled Canada, and Spain still owned the land that is now Florida.

During the Revolutionary War, a group wrote a plan of government called the *Articles of Confederation.* This plan provided for a weak national government and strong state governments. During the war, the new states had been willing to work together to fight the British. After the war, the government under the Articles of Confederation could not solve all the problems of the new country. Changes had to be made to the plan.

Finally, in May 1787, all the states except Rhode Island agreed to send delegates to a Constitutional Convention. This convention was held in Philadelphia, Pennsylvania. George Washington was chosen president of the convention.

The Constitutional Convention ended in September 1787. For four months, the delegates discussed and argued over what was the best form of government for the young country. At times, it appeared that the Convention would break up. Eventually, the Constitution was completed. Many compromises had been made.

The Constitution is the supreme, or highest, law of government. Three branches of government were established by the Constitution. The executive branch (the President) enforces the laws. The legislative branch (Congress) makes the laws. Finally, the judicial branch (the courts) interprets the law. Each branch is separate and can check and balance the actions of the other two.

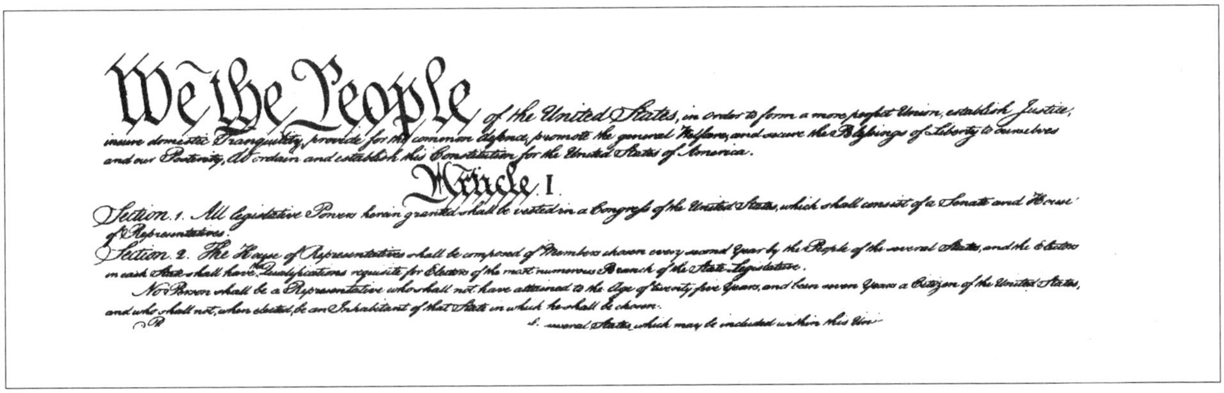

We the People of the United States, in Order to form a more perfect Union, establish Justice, insure domestic Tranquility, provide for the common defence, promote the general Welfare, and secure the Blessings of Liberty to ourselves and our Posterity, do ordain and establish this Constitution for the United States of America.

Article I.

Section. 1. All legislative Powers herein granted shall be vested in a Congress of the United States, which shall consist of a Senate and House of Representatives.

Section. 2. The House of Representatives shall be composed of Members chosen every second Year by the People of the several States, and the Electors in each State shall have the Qualifications requisite for Electors of the most numerous Branch of the State Legislature.

No Person shall be a Representative who shall not have attained to the Age of twenty five Years, and been seven Years a Citizen of the United States, and who shall not, when elected, be an Inhabitant of that State in which he shall be chosen.

... several States which may be included within this Union

**The Constitution**

Some Americans believed the Constitution did not protect their rights. They wanted their rights listed in the Constitution. Ten amendments, changes or additions, called the *Bill of Rights,* were added to the Constitution in 1791. Freedom of speech, religion, and the press; the right to a jury trial; and other rights were now guaranteed, or protected, under the Constitution.

Also included in the Constitution was the right of states to have their own governments. The states would be able to manage many of their own affairs. In our federal system of government, the power to govern is divided between the central government and the state governments. This division of power was a bold new experiment in government. For over two hundred years, it has served our country very well.

**Famous Americans**

This Virginian was a surveyor, the owner of a large farm, and a soldier. He presided over the Constitutional Convention. Soon after, he became the first President of the United States of America. While he was President, the Bill of Rights was added to the Constitution.

Our country's capital city is named after him, and he is often called the "Father of Our Country." You know him in part because he was the leader of the colonial army during the Revolutionary War.

Write his name on the line under his picture. ______________________

This Virginian worked as a lawyer. He was chosen as a Virginia delegate to the Continental Congress and also to the Constitutional Convention. He helped write the new Constitution. He promised that liberty would be safe under the Constitution. He kept one of the most complete records of activities during the Constitutional Convention. He helped draft the Bill of Rights and helped write *The Federalist,* a published series of letters that supported adopting the Constitution. Therefore, he is sometimes called the "Father of the Constitution." In 1808, he was elected as the fourth President of the United States.

Write his name on the line under his picture. ______________________

## What Did You Find Out?

**A** Read the words and dates in the box below. Choose the words or date that best completes each sentence. Write your answers on the lines.

| | | |
|---|---|---|
| 1783 | Constitution | Bill of Rights |
| 1787 | Treaty of Paris | Constitutional Convention |
| 1791 | George Washington | Articles of Confederation |

1. The treaty that ended the Revolutionary War was called the ______________________.
2. The British recognized Americans' independence in the year ______________________.
3. The ______________________ provided a plan of government during the Revolutionary War.
4. The ______________________ was held in Philadelphia in the year ______________________ to make changes in the national government.
5. ______________________was chosen to serve as the president of the Constitutional Convention.
6. The delegates had written a new ______________________ by the time the convention ended.
7. In the year ______________________, the ______________________ was added to the Constitution to protect the personal rights and freedoms of Americans.

**B** The Constitution established three branches of government. Write the name of each branch below. Then describe the job that each branch does.

**Congress**

a. Branch ____________________

b. Job ____________________

____________________

**President**

c. Branch ____________________

d. Job ____________________

____________________

**Courts**

e. Branch ____________________

f. Job ____________________

____________________

UNIT 3

# The United States Grows



In 1789, the United States extended from the Atlantic Ocean on the east, to the Mississippi River on the west. The country shared its northern boundary with Canada, and Spain owned Florida. Our country was about one-third as large as it is now. How did the United States grow larger?

The Louisiana Territory was the first large area of land to be added. It was added in 1803. Thomas Jefferson was the President at the time. He wanted to buy some land from Emperor Napoleon of France. To his surprise, Napoleon offered to sell all of the Louisiana Territory for 15 million dollars. This area included 827,987 square miles (2,144,476 square kilometers). President Jefferson quickly agreed. Through this purchase, the United States doubled in size.

In 1818, President James Monroe had problems with Spanish-owned Florida. To settle the problems, he sent General Andrew Jackson to Florida with an army that quickly seized the colonial capital. The Spanish surrendered to General Jackson. In 1819, Spain sold Florida to the United States for five million dollars. Again, the United States grew larger.

Americans began exploring lands west of the Mississippi after the Louisiana Territory was bought. President Jefferson asked Meriwether Lewis and William Clark to lead a group of explorers to explore the Oregon Country as well as the northern Louisiana Territory. Zebulon Pike explored the southern territories, including New Mexico, which belonged to Spain. Before long, other Americans were traveling to lands west of the Louisiana Territory.

In the 1820s, Mexicans revolted against their Spanish rulers. They won their independence. At that time, Mexican lands included what are now Texas and much of the southwestern United States. Some Americans began to settle in the Mexican territory of Texas. Before long, disagreements arose between the American settlers and the Mexican authorities. They fought each other, and the Americans won. They declared Texas an independent nation in 1836. The Texans applied to make Texas part of the United States. Finally, early in 1845, it became a state.

James Polk became President in 1845. He and many others believed that our country should stretch from the Atlantic Ocean on the east to the Pacific Ocean on the west. This belief was called *Manifest Destiny.* Several problems developed between the United States and Mexico. The countries argued over boundaries as well as the rights of American settlers on Mexican lands. President Polk sent troops to Texas. In 1846, the Mexican army attacked American soldiers stationed near the Rio Grande. This attack started a war between the United States and Mexico. In 1848, Mexico surrendered. A treaty resulted in what was called the *Mexican Cession.* Mexico gave up most of its land between Texas and the Pacific Ocean in return for 15 million dollars. The United States now reached from ocean to ocean, just as President Polk said it should.

A little earlier, in 1846, an agreement was made with Britain for part of the Oregon Territory. President Polk agreed to a compromise to avoid a possible war with England. Later, in 1853, the United States bought a small area of Mexican land that today makes up southern New Mexico and Arizona. This purchase, known as the Gadsden Purchase, gave the United States a good area through which to build a railroad route to southern California.

Two other important additions came later. During Andrew Johnson's term as President, Secretary of State William Seward bought Alaska from Russia in 1867 for $7,200,000. Then in the year 1898, Hawaii became a territory of the United States.

The thirteen original states, small in size, had grown to be the fourth largest country in the world. Only Russia, Canada, and China have more land than the United States.

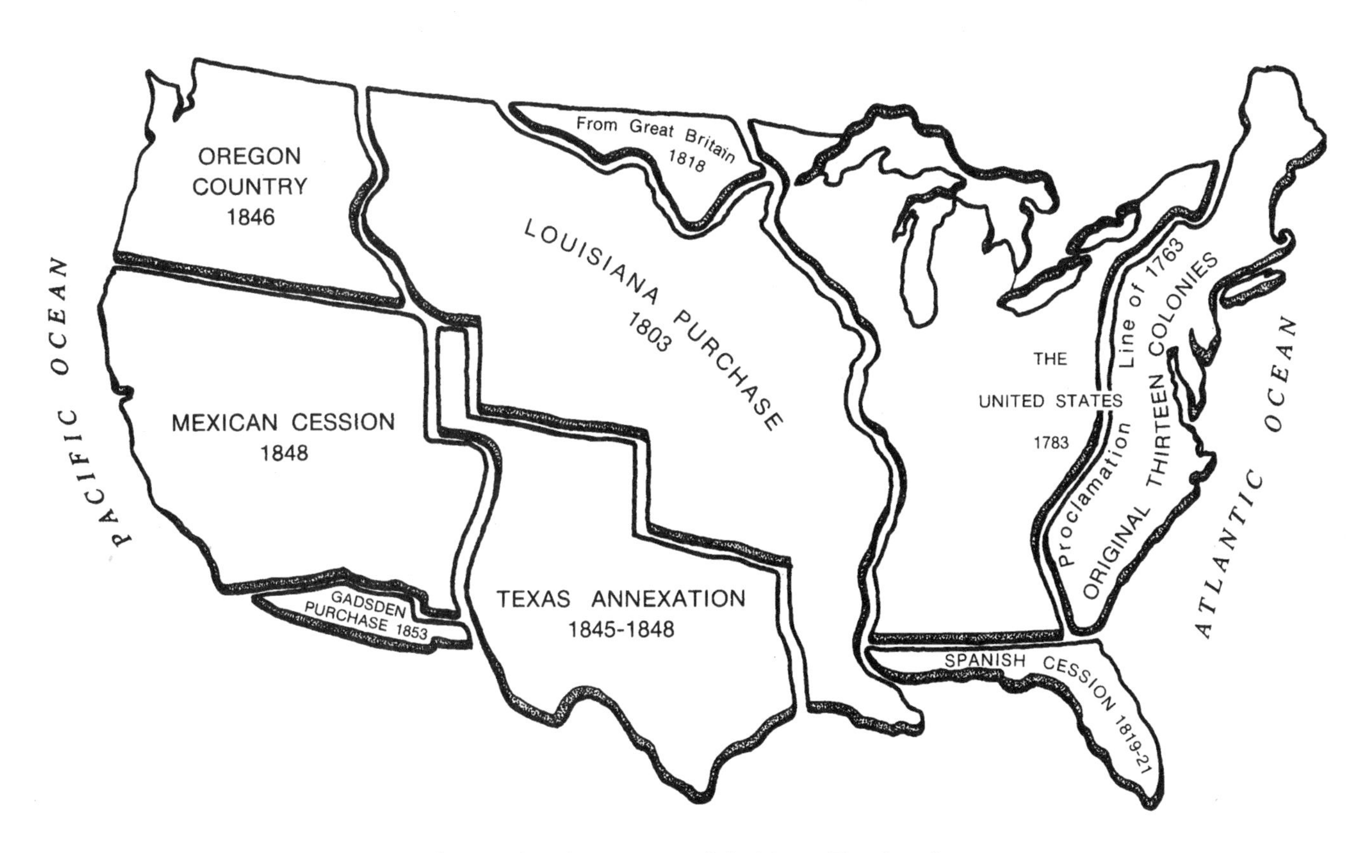


**The United States Adds New Territories**

UNIT 3

1. Delaware 1787
2. Pennsylvania 1787
3. New Jersey 1787
4. Georgia 1788
5. Connecticut 1788
6. Massachusetts 1788
7. Maryland 1788
8. South Carolina 1788
9. New Hampshire 1788
10. Virginia 1788
11. New York 1788
12. North Carolina 1789
13. Rhode Island 1790
14. Vermont 1791
15. Kentucky 1792
16. Tennessee 1796
17. Ohio 1803
18. Louisiana 1812
19. Indiana 1816
20. Mississippi 1817
21. Illinois 1818
22. Alabama 1819
23. Maine 1820
24. Missouri 1821
25. Arkansas 1836
26. Michigan 1837
27. Florida 1845
28. Texas 1845
29. Iowa 1846
30. Wisconsin 1848
31. California 1850
32. Minnesota 1858
33. Oregon 1859
34. Kansas 1861
35. West Virginia 1863
36. Nevada 1864
37. Nebraska 1867
38. Colorado 1876
39. North Dakota 1889
40. South Dakota 1889
41. Montana 1889
42. Washington 1889
43. Idaho 1890
44. Wyoming 1890
45. Utah 1896
46. Oklahoma 1907
47. New Mexico 1912
48. Arizona 1912
49. Alaska 1959
50. Hawaii 1959

**The United States**

Study the map and chart. Then answer the following questions.

1. What is the name of your state? ______________________
2. In what year did it become a state? ______________________
3. What number was it? (1, 50, etc.) ______________________
4. Was it one of the original thirteen states? ______________________
5. Was your state in one of the territories? ______________________

   If so, which one? ______________________

**American History Time Line**
Turn to the American History Time Line on page 93. On line 5, write "The United States grows larger."

## What Did You Find Out?

**A** Describe the event that occurred on each of the following dates.

1. 1803 ______________________
2. 1819 ______________________
3. 1846 ______________________
4. 1848 ______________________
5. 1867 ______________________
6. 1898 ______________________

**B** Match the areas of land in column 1 with the descriptions in column 2.

| | Column 1 | Column 2 |
|---|---|---|
| ______ | 1. Oregon Territory | a. enabled the United States to reach from ocean to ocean |
| ______ | 2. Florida | b. doubled the size of the United States |
| ______ | 3. Mexican Cession | c. enabled a railroad to be built to California |
| ______ | 4. Alaska | d. acquired from Britain |
| ______ | 5. Gadsden Purchase | e. became a territory in 1898 |
| ______ | 6. Hawaii | f. purchased for five million dollars from Spain |
| ______ | 7. Louisiana Purchase | g. purchased for $7,200,000 from Russia |

**C** Identify each of the following people. Write a sentence that describes the role each played in helping the United States grow larger.

1. Thomas Jefferson ______________________
2. Napoleon ______________________
3. James Monroe ______________________
4. Andrew Jackson ______________________
5. James Polk ______________________
6. William Seward ______________________
7. Andrew Johnson ______________________

# The American West



Our country grew by expanding, or adding land. At first, these lands were called *territories*. Most of these territories were later divided into smaller pieces called *states*.

At first, very few Americans lived in the new territories. Most still lived in the thirteen original states. Gradually, people began to move into the new territories. As you can see from your map on page 31, they moved from the east side of our country to the west side. They first moved across the Appalachians into territory east of the Mississippi. There they found good farmland. Then they began pushing west of the Mississippi River.

Americans began to move to the western part of the United States in the mid-1800s. Like Americans, immigrants traveled west, too. Immigrants are people who came to the United States from other countries, such as Germany, Ireland, and England.

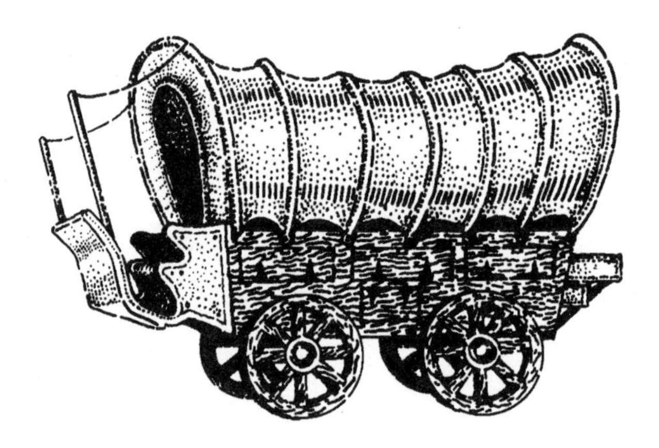

**A Covered Wagon**

### Wagons West

A group of pioneers are talking to one another as they prepare to leave Independence, Missouri, for the long journey west. Read the conversation to find out why some people moved west.

*Pioneer 1:* Where are you and your family heading?

*Pioneer 2:* We plan to go almost to Astoria, Oregon, in our covered wagon. We want to start a new life as farmers in a new land. We heard that Oregon has rich resources, and we can get cheap farmland. Our trail boss will lead us and others over the Oregon Trail.

*Pioneer 1:* Did you know Astoria was founded as a trading post by fur trappers? They went west to trap fur and trade with the Indians. They were the first people from the United States to live and work in the Far West.

*Pioneer 2:* I heard you and your friend say that you are on your way to California. I suppose you hope to find gold.

*Pioneer 1:* Yes, we do. Ever since gold was discovered at Sutter's Mill in 1848, we've been planning to go to California and stake a claim. We'll take the Oregon Trail west until it meets up with the California Trail and then we'll travel that trail to Fort Sutter.

People moved west for many different reasons. Some were missionaries who hoped to convert the Indians. Some, like the Mormons, traveled west in search of a place where they could worship freely. The Mormons found that place in Utah. Some were adventurers lured by the unknown. Most were people hoping to improve their lives.

These pioneers traveled across the Great Plains, but few thought of settling there. It had been called the *Great American Desert.* Eventually, however, people began settling the plains. They found that it was a good place to raise wheat. More people were lured there by cheap land. In 1862, Congress passed the Homestead Act. It gave families 160 acres of land almost free. The head of the family had to live on the land for five years. Especially after the Civil War and with the building of the transcontinental railroads, more and more people headed west.

As thousands of pioneers moved west, they settled on land that belonged to the Indians. The lands were taken away from the Indians, and they were forced to live on reservations, or areas set aside for Indian use. Disagreements over the land and forcing Indians to live on reservations resulted in many Indian Wars. Although the Indians tried to defend their lands, they could not stop the tide of settlers streaming into their homelands. The Indian way of life was changed forever. Before long, the West was dotted with farms, ranches, and towns.

### Famous Americans

This famous pioneer from Tennessee was a hunter who grew up on the frontier, or the edge of settled territory. Although he knew little about making laws, he was elected to work for our government three times. He did very well working in Congress just by using his common sense and honesty. Because he wore a suit made from deerskin and a hat made from the skin of a raccoon, the other lawmakers in Washington called him the "Coonskin Congressman." One of his famous sayings is: "Be always sure you're right, then go ahead." After being defeated for re-election in 1835, he went to Texas. There he helped Texans fight for independence. He was among those who died defending the Alamo in San Antonio.

This man's first name was "Davy." Do you know his last name? Write it on the line.

______________________

### What Did You Find Out?

Complete the following questions.

1. People went west for many reasons. Write four of these reasons on the lines below.
   a. ______________________
   b. ______________________
   c. ______________________
   d. ______________________

2. Not all pioneers went to the same places in the West. List three different places they went.
   a. ______________________
   b. ______________________
   c. ______________________

3. Many of the people who went west were new to our country.
   a. What were these peoples called? ______________________
   b. List three countries from which these people came. ______________________

______________________

4. Tell how pioneers could get nearly free land.
   a. What law made the nearly free land available? ______________________
   b. How much free land could a settler get? ______________________
   c. Who said settlers could have this land? ______________________

5. What did the Indians try to do as others began settling on their lands?

______________________

6. Where were many Indians forced to live after the pioneers took their land?

______________________

7. Would you have liked to have moved west? Tell why or why not. Write your answer in complete sentences.

______________________

______________________

______________________

______________________

______________________

8. Describe five items you would have taken with you on your journey west. Think about what would be necessary to survive and to start a new life. Remember that some items are hard to carry long distances on a horse or in a wagon.

______________________

______________________

______________________

______________________

______________________

______________________

# The United States Is Divided



Between 1860 and 1865, our country was divided into two parts. War broke out between people in the Northern states and people in the Southern states. Fighting between the people who live in the same country is called a *civil war.* The Civil War in the United States is also called the *War Between the States* because the Northern states and the Southern states fought against each other.

You will learn some of the reasons for this war by finding out more about the Northern and Southern states. Look at the map. It shows how our country was divided during the Civil War. Knowing how the North and South were different will help you understand why the Civil War happened.

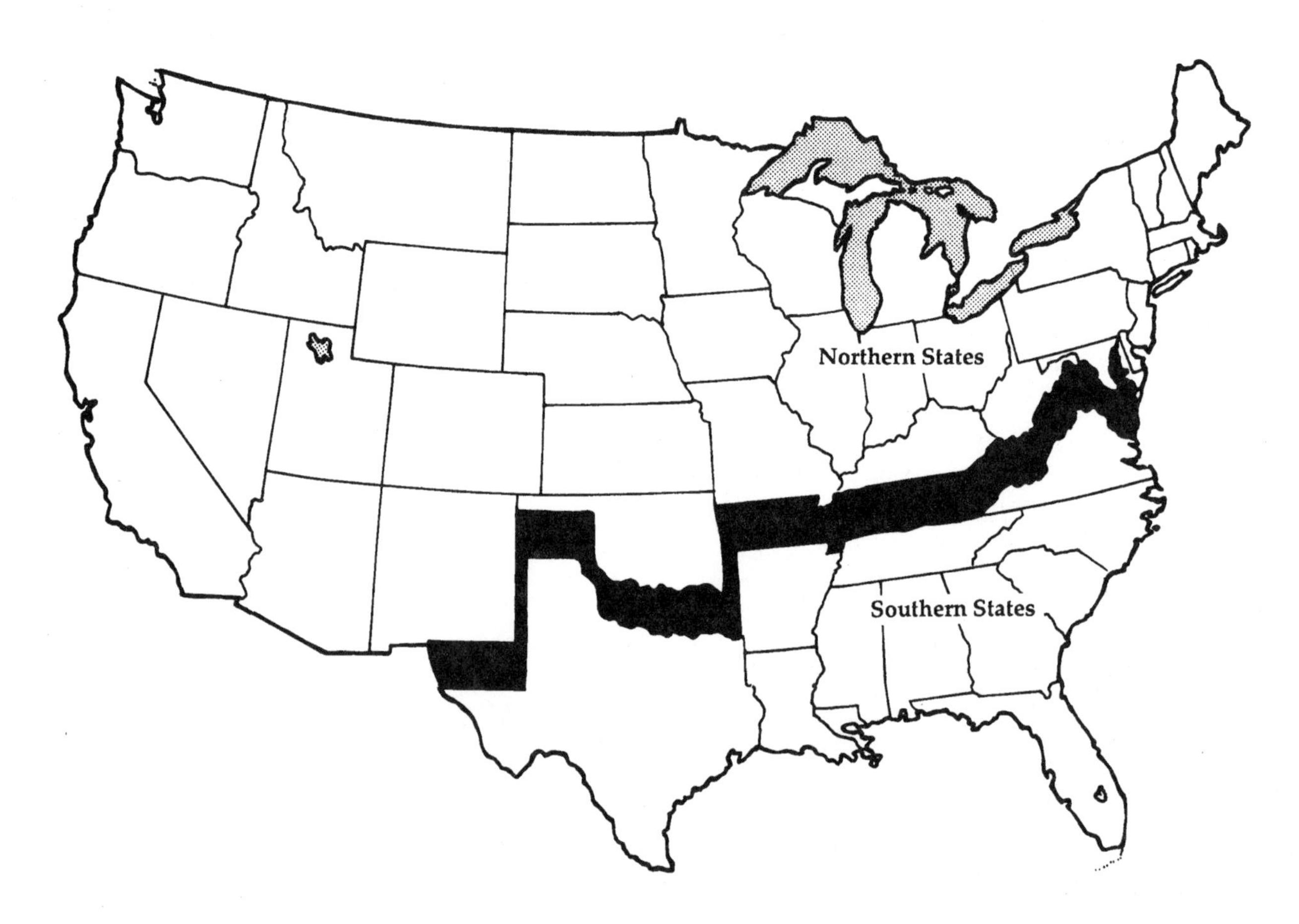


**The Northern and the Southern States**

### The North

The Northern states had many industries. Many people worked in factories and shipyards. People in the North were very proud of their factories. Our government helped the factory owners by adding a tax to the items Americans bought from other countries including Britain. This tax made goods shipped from Britain cost more than goods made in the United States. Therefore, people in the United States bought what they needed from the factories in the North. Most people in the North liked the tax. The increase in sales helped them make more money.

**The Northern (Union) Flag**

Many people in the North were factory workers. Many were immigrants who came to the United States to make a better life for themselves. People in the North did not believe that workers should be slaves. Many thought that no part of the United States should have slaves.

Many people worked to end slavery. They were called *abolitionists,* because they wanted to abolish, or end, slavery. One abolitionist Harriet Beecher Stowe wrote *Uncle Tom's Cabin,* which was an antislavery novel. Through her book, she tried to make people aware of the injustices of slavery.

### The South

The South had very few factories. Most people lived and worked on small farms. Some people owned and operated very large farms, called *plantations.* Cotton was a major crop on many plantations. Large numbers of people were needed to work on these plantations. Many of the workers were enslaved African Americans. Plantation owners said that they could not afford to operate the plantations without slaves. Plantations could not grow cotton without the help of many slaves. Wealthy people in the South also liked to buy the things they needed from Britain. Until the tax was added, Britain's goods cost less than goods made in the North. The plantation owners did not like the tax.

**The Southern (Confederate) Flag**

Many people had hoped that the differences between the North and the South could be settled without fighting. They did not want to see their country divided. One of these people was Abraham Lincoln.

Abraham Lincoln was elected President in 1860. He hoped to resolve the problems between the North and the South. The South did not trust Abraham Lincoln. Southerners were afraid that he would free the slaves. Some Southern states seceded from, or left, the Union. They set up a new country called the *Confederate States of America.* Jefferson Davis was chosen to be president of the Confederate States.

On March 4, 1861, Abraham Lincoln took office as the President of the United States. President Lincoln wished that war could be avoided. He talked of peace. He hoped that the Southern states would come back into the Union. However, both the North and the South were organizing their armies and preparing for war.

The North had a plan to defeat the Southern states. It was called the *Anaconda Plan.* An anaconda is a very large snake that squeezes its prey to death. The North planned to blockade, or stop, all shipping into the South. This blockade would gradually force the Confederacy to surrender.

Meanwhile, the South had a plan of its own. General Robert E. Lee was an outstanding leader. His plan was to wait for the North to attack. He believed that Southerners would fight to protect their land.

Four long years of fighting took place. Both the Northern Yankees and Southern Rebels lost thousands of troops. Finally, the Northern army, led by General Ulysses S. Grant, defeated General Robert E. Lee. Lee surrendered on April 9, 1865, at Appomattox Court House in Virginia. The Civil War was over.

The month before, in his second inaugural address, Lincoln called for a generous peace by saying, "With malice toward none, with charity for all, with firmness in the right as God gives us to see the right, let us strive to finish the work we are in, to bind up the nation's wounds . . . to do all which may achieve . . . a just and lasting peace." After the surrender by Lee, Lincoln welcomed the South back into the Union. How Lincoln would have healed the nation's wounds will never be known. Five days after Lee surrendered, John Wilkes Booth shot Lincoln as he watched a play. On April 15, 1865, Lincoln died.

Life in the South was very hard after the war ended. Homes, towns, farms, and plantations had been destroyed. There was little food. Many of the South's leaders were put into prison. To help rebuild the South, the government passed a plan for Reconstruction. Unfortunately, the plan did not work very well.

Slowly, the former Confederate States began to rebuild. Little by little, the South began to raise crops and sell goods again. Eventually, our country was once again united.

**American History Time Line**
Turn to the American History Time Line on page 93. On line 6, write "The Civil War divides the nation."

**Famous Americans**

This American author was born in Connecticut in 1811. She was a very religious woman who was passionately against slavery. She is best known for her novel, *Uncle Tom's Cabin.* This book, published in 1851, tried to show the cruelty and immorality of slavery. More than any other book, this novel intensified the disagreements between the North and the South over the issue of slavery.

Southerners protested her antislavery novel. The author wrote another book with a similar viewpoint, *Dred: A Tale of the Great Dismal Swamp.* In addition, she wrote essays, biographies, and children's stories.

Do you know this famous American author? Write her name on the line under her picture.

______________________________

**Famous Americans**

This famous woman was born in Massachusetts in 1821. As a young woman, she was a school teacher. During the Civil War, she became very concerned because wounded soldiers were not getting good care. Soon she began helping these soldiers. Because she worked so hard caring for the wounded from both the North and South, she was called the "Angel of the Battlefield."

In 1881, she set up the American Red Cross and became its first president. Today the American Red Cross is still helping people during times of war, floods, and storms.

Who is this famous American woman? If you do not know, copy each letter underlined above in order. Write your answer on the line under her picture.

______________________________

UNIT 3

## What Did You Find Out?

**A** Read the words and phrases in the box below. Write the words or phrases that best describe the North under *Northern States.* Write the words or phrases that best describe the South under *Southern States.*

| | | | | |
|---|---|---|---|---|
| slaves | liked tax | free people | factories | Rebels |
| plantations | Lee | Yankees | Grant | did not like tax |

| Northern States | Southern States |
|---|---|
| 1. ______________ | 6. ______________ |
| 2. ______________ | 7. ______________ |
| 3. ______________ | 8. ______________ |
| 4. ______________ | 9. ______________ |
| 5. ______________ | 10. ______________ |

**B** Put these sentences in the correct order. Write 1, 2, 3, etc., on the lines.

_____ The United States grows larger.

_____ The colonies become free after the Revolutionary War.

_____ Only Indians live in North America.

_____ Europeans explore the Americas.

_____ The Civil War takes place.

_____ Jamestown is settled.

**C** Write *True* or *False* on the line before each statement.

______________ **1.** Abraham Lincoln was from the South.

______________ **2.** The North won the Civil War.

______________ **3.** Another name for the Civil War is the War Between the States.

______________ **4.** The leader of the North's army was Jefferson Davis.

______________ **5.** The president of the Confederate States was Robert E. Lee.

UNIT 3

**D** Write your answers in the blanks.

1. A ____________ war involves fighting between people of the same country.
2. Abraham Lincoln took office as President in the year ____________.
3. Some Southern states had already ____________, or left, the Union by the time Lincoln took office.
4. Look at the map on page 38. List the eleven states that formed the Confederacy.

   a. ____________ g. ____________

   b. ____________ h. ____________

   c. ____________ i. ____________

   d. ____________ j. ____________

   e. ____________ k. ____________

   f. ____________

5. The North was going to use the ____________ Plan to defeat the South.
6. Northerners hoped to ____________ all shipping into the South.
7. The North believed that the South would be forced to ____________.
8. ____________ wanted to wait for the North to attack the South.
9. He believed that Southerners would fight to ____________ their land.
10. The Civil War lasted ____________ years.
11. The war ended in the year ____________.
12. General ____________ of the North defeated General ____________.
13. General Lee surrendered at ____________ on April 9, 1865.
14. President Lincoln died from a gunshot wound on ____________.
15. Why was it very hard for the South to rebuild and rejoin the union after the Civil War ended?

____________________________________________

R E V I E W

# Review Units 1–3

**A** The sentences below review the main ideas that you have studied in Units 1–3. Complete the sentences. Write your answers on the lines provided.

1. At first, only ________________________ lived in North America.
2. European ________________________ sailed to the Americas.
3. The Spanish had colonies in ________________________ and ________________________.
4. The British established ________________________ colonies in North America.
5. These colonies sold most of their lumber and furs to ________________________.
6. One of the king's laws said that the colonists had to pay ________________________ on the items they bought from Britain.
7. The ________________________ was a document written to the king. It said that the colonists wanted to be free.
8. The ________________________ was the war between Britain and the American colonies.
9. After this war, the colonies called their new country the ________________________.
10. Soon the states set up a new central government by writing the ________________________.
11. Later, ten amendments, called the ________________________, were added.
12. The United States grew by adding areas of land called ________________________, which later became ________________________.
13. ________________________ is the name given to people who come from other countries to live in the United States.
14. Western expansion took much Indian land. Many Indians went to live on land set aside for them called ________________________.
15. Later, the ________________________ states and the ________________________ states began to fight.
16. This fighting was called the ________________________ War.
17. The ________________________ eventually won the war.
18. The plan for ________________________ of the South did not work very well.

REVIEW

**B** You have learned about many people in America's history. Read the description of each person. Write the correct names on the lines provided.

1. My ship was the first to go around the world. ______________________
2. I warned the colonists that the British soldiers were marching to Lexington and Concord.

   ______________________
3. I wrote the Declaration of Independence in 1776. ______________________
4. I was the King of Great Britain during the Revolutionary War. ______________________
5. I was the first President of the United States. ______________________
6. I am sometimes called the "Father of the Constitution." ______________________
7. I was a famous pioneer and hunter. I became a Congressman. ______________________
8. As President, I believed that the United States should extend from ocean to ocean.

   ______________________
9. During the Civil War, I helped wounded soldiers from both the North and the South. Later I set up the American Red Cross. ______________________.
10. I wrote *Uncle Tom's Cabin.* ______________________
11. I was president of the Confederacy. ______________________
12. I was commander of the Northern army during the Civil War. ______________________
13. I was commander of the Southern army during the Civil War. ______________________
14. I was President of the United States during the Civil War. ______________________

## Machines Change Life In the United States



At first, people in the United States did most of their work by hand. They sewed their own clothes. They made their own chairs, tables, and even houses. Most Americans knew how to use their hands very well. When they wanted or needed something, they usually made it themselves.

Often they could not afford to buy factory-made things. Most factories were very small. Factories made only a few of the things Americans wanted and needed.

Most farms were small, too. There were few machines to help farmers do the work. Crops had to be planted, cared for, and harvested by hand. Most Americans worked very hard on these small farms.

**The Cotton Gin**

In the early 1800s, however, people found new ways to do work. They built many new machines. Machines often can do work easier and faster. The people who built these machines were called *inventors.* Inventors built many new machines to do the work that had been done by hand before. For example, on cotton plantations, slaves separated cotton seeds from the fiber by hand. The work was very hard and time consuming. After the cotton gin was invented, it was used to separate the seeds and fiber. The cotton gin made it possible for plantation owners to grow and process more cotton.

Eventually, inventors made and improved other kinds of farm machines, such as the reaper, combine, and tractor. These machines helped farmers plow, plant, and harvest crops faster than they could by hand. New farm machines meant that more crops could be grown by fewer people.

**A Reaper**

Inventors also made factory machines; for example, sewing machines, saws, and drills. Factory machines could make things faster than people could make them by hand. Because they could be made faster, they were also cheaper. More Americans could afford to buy factory-made clothes, chairs, and many other things.

By the time the Civil War ended, industries were growing. Many new factories were built. In a short time, factories were making hundreds of products for Americans to buy.

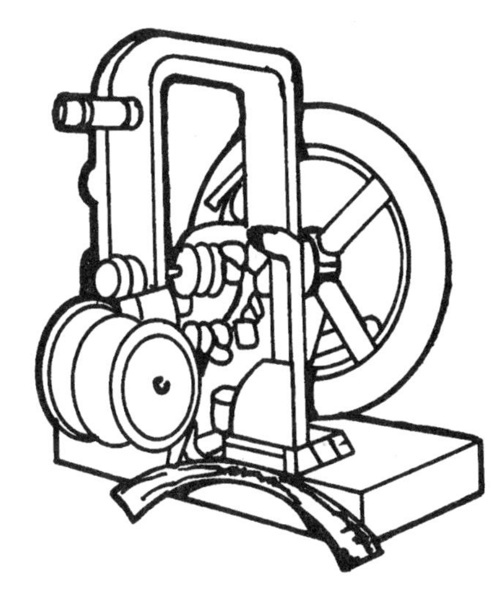

An Early Sewing Machine

As the number of factories grew, they needed many more workers. Because fewer people were needed to do farm work, many Americans left the farms and rural areas. They moved to places near factories and factory jobs. The small towns around factories became larger cities.

Soon cities became crowded. People had trouble finding places to live. Because so many people were crowded together, many parts of cities became rundown and dirty. These poorer parts of a city were called *slums.* Life in the slums was, and still is, a big problem in American cities.

Factory workers did not have a good life. They were paid very little. They had to work many hours each day. Factory buildings were dark. The air inside factories was often filled with dirt, dust, and smoke. Machines in the factories were not always safe to use.

After many years, factory workers decided that they had to do something about their low pay and the bad places where they worked. They began to join together in groups. These groups of workers were called *labor unions.* Labor unions asked factory owners for better pay and better conditions in the factories.

At first, factory owners did not listen to the unions. This made the workers angry. Sometimes workers became so angry that they began fighting with the owners. Little by little, factory owners and labor unions learned to settle their differences without fighting.

If an agreement could not be reached, the workers would stop working in the factory. This action is called a *strike.* During a strike, factory workers walk in front of the factory building. They carry signs that say the factory owner is not being fair to them. This action is called *picketing.* The workers usually do not go back to work until the union and factory owners settle their differences.

Today workers and owners try to talk over their differences before a strike is called. Sometimes they ask another person to listen to both sides and to make a fair decision. This person is called an *arbitrator.* The arbitrator gives what he or she thinks is a fair solution to both sides.

UNIT 4

Over the years, labor unions have helped workers in many ways. Workers make better pay. They work in cleaner, safer factories. They do not have to work so many hours. Giant factories now make things faster, easier, and cheaper than ever before. For these reasons, most Americans are able to buy cars, television sets, and many other products. Machines have done much to change life in the United States.

**An Early Automobile**

The government also has passed laws to help make factories cleaner and safer for all Americans. Products must be tested to be sure that they are made properly and are safe to use. Factories are not allowed to pollute or spoil rivers, large bodies of water, land, or air. Workers are also protected against harmful materials; for example, asbestos or dangerous chemicals. Vacations, pensions, and medical insurance are often provided by many companies and factories to give more security and a better life to the workers.

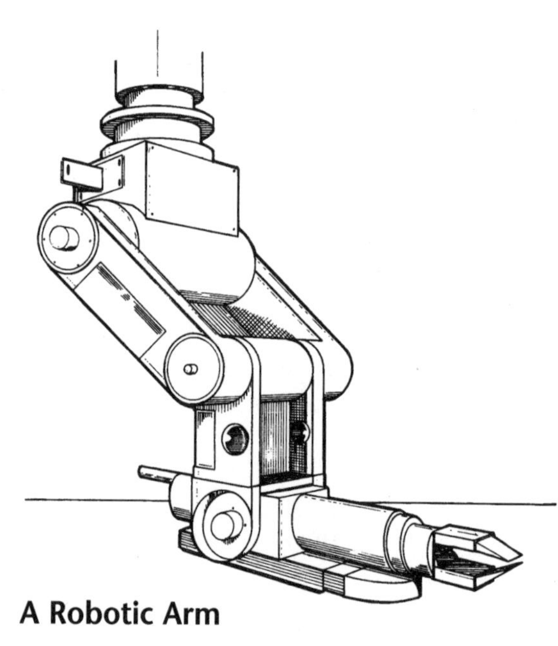

**A Robotic Arm**

American factories, however, face a great challenge. Many other countries are now producing the same kinds of products that our factories make. Not as many workers are needed in factories today. Many traditional jobs are now done by machines. For example, robots can be used to help build cars. Computers are used to program these new machines to do the jobs workers once did. This process is called *automation.*

Our country is still the largest industrial country in the world. In the years to come, our industries and workers will need to do more to make products better, safer, faster, and cheaper than ever before.

**American History Time Line**

Turn to the American History Time Line on page 93. On line 7, write "Factories and cities grow."

**Famous Americans**

During the 1800s, inventors also found better ways of sending messages. One of these inventors made a machine that could send messages quickly by using dots (• •) and dashes (– –) to stand for letters of the alphabet. He got the idea for his invention while sailing home from Europe. Being an artist, he first drew pictures of his new invention. When he got home, he quickly made his invention from an old clock, a picture frame, and pieces of wood and wire.

You will find this inventor's dot and dash code on this page. Use it to discover the name of this famous inventor and the name of his invention. The first letter is done for you. When you have finished, write his name on the line under his picture.

________________________

| CODE | | | | |
|---|---|---|---|---|
| A • – | B – • • • | C • • • | D – • • | E • |
| F • – • | G – – • | H • • • • | I • • | J – • – • |
| K – • – | L — | M – – | N – • | O • • |
| P • • • • • | Q • • – • | R • • • | S • • • | T – |
| U • • – | V • • • – | W • – – | X • – • • | Y • • • • |
| Z • • • • | | | | |

| • • • | • – | – – | • • – | • | — |
|---|---|---|---|---|---|
| S | | | | | |

| – – | • • | • • • | • • • | • |
|---|---|---|---|---|
| | | | | |

| • • | – • | • • • – | • | – • | – | • | – • • |
|---|---|---|---|---|---|---|---|
| | | | | | | | |

| – | • • • • | • |
|---|---|---|
| | | |

| – | • | — | • | – – • | • • • | • – | • • • • • | • • • • |
|---|---|---|---|---|---|---|---|---|
| | | | | | | | | |

UNIT 4

## What Did You Find Out?

**A** Write in the word or words that best complete each statement.

1. At first, the United States was a country of many small ______________________ and few ______________________.
2. Inventors built new and improved ______________________ that did work that had previously been done by hand.
3. As Americans began buying more and more machine-made products, ______________________ began to grow.
4. As people moved near factory jobs, small towns became large ______________________.
5. Factory workers joined together in labor ______________________ to get better pay and better conditions in factories.

**B** Answer each of the following questions. Use complete sentences.

1. Do you think farm inventions had any effect on the sizes of farms? Why or why not?

______________________________________________________________

______________________________________________________________

2. Name three inventions that made farming easier.

______________________________________________________________

3. Why did factories begin to grow? ______________________________________________

______________________________________________________________

4. How did small towns become large cities? ______________________________________

______________________________________________________________

5. What are two reasons why factory workers joined together in unions?

   a. ______________________________________________________________

   b. ______________________________________________________________

6. What are three ways in which the United States changed during the 1800s?

   a. ______________________________________________________________

   b. ______________________________________________________________

   c. ______________________________________________________________

## C Match the words in column 1 with their meanings in column 2.

| | Column 1 | Column 2 |
|---|---|---|
| ______ | 1. inventors | a. dirty, rundown parts of cities |
| ______ | 2. arbitrator | b. walking in front of factory buildings with signs saying the factory is unfair to workers |
| ______ | 3. slums | c. to stop all work in a factory to protest job conditions |
| ______ | 4. picketing | d. people who made new and improved machines and tools |
| ______ | 5. strike | e. a third person who listens to both sides |

## D Circle the letter of the correct answer.

1. The cotton gin was used to
   a. pick cotton.
   b. plant cotton.
   c. separate cotton seeds from the fiber.
2. An example of a factory machine is a
   a. reaper.
   b. tractor.
   c. sewing machine.
3. In this lesson, you have learned how the United States became
   a. more like the country you know today.
   b. a larger country.
   c. less like the country you know today.
4. Labor unions helped workers get
   a. better pay.
   b. their own factories.
   c. longer working hours.

**A Factory Worker in the Early 1800s**

## E Explain what each of the following words means. Use complete sentences. If necessary, look up the words in a dictionary.

1. factory ______________________________
2. pollute ______________________________
3. pension ______________________________
4. computers ______________________________
5. automation ______________________________

UNIT 4

# The United States Becomes a Stronger Country



At the same time that its factories, farms, and cities were growing in size, the United States also became a larger and stronger country. It grew in population and in area. The leading nations of the world also began to recognize the importance of the country in world affairs.

You have already learned how the United States expanded from the Atlantic Ocean to the Pacific Ocean. Its population was also growing during this time. By 1890, the population had increased to nearly 63 million. New York City had a population of over 3 million. Both Chicago and Philadelphia had passed the one million mark in population.

Following the Civil War, the United States added on land by purchasing Alaska from Russia. In 1867, the United States decided to buy Alaska for 7.2 million dollars. Many Americans thought that buying Alaska was a poor use of money. Americans soon learned, however, that this land was rich in gold, lumber, fish, and furs. Today it is also a rich source of oil. In 1959, Alaska became our forty-ninth and largest state.

Hawaiian Pineapple

In 1898, the Hawaiian Islands became a territory of the United States. An island is a small body of land with water all around it. Hawaii is famous for its pineapples, coffee, and sugar. In 1959, these islands became our fiftieth state.

The European country of Spain owned and controlled many islands in the Caribbean Sea and in the Pacific Ocean. Look at the map on page 54. You will see that the Caribbean Sea is southeast of the United States, and the Pacific Ocean is west of the United States. Problems occurred in Cuba, a major Spanish-controlled island in the Caribbean Sea. Eventually, these problems caused the United States to take action.

On February 15, 1898, the American battleship *Maine* was blown up in the harbor at Havana, Cuba. In April of that year, President William McKinley asked Congress to declare war against Spain. The Spanish-American War ended in just a few months. Spain had to grant Cuba its freedom. It also gave Puerto Rico, Guam, and the Philippines to the United States. The peace treaty required the United States to pay 20 million dollars to Spain for the Philippines. At that same time in 1898, Congress voted to add Hawaii as a territory of the United States. Later, the United States acquired the Samoan islands in the Pacific Ocean (1899) and the Virgin Islands in the Caribbean Sea (1916). The Spanish-American War was the first event that made the United States a world power.

Another important event that made the United States a world power was the building of the Panama Canal. President Theodore Roosevelt acquired a ten-mile strip of land in Panama in 1903. A canal was built to link the Atlantic Ocean and the Pacific Ocean. Ships would save 8,000 miles by going through the canal rather than sailing all the way around South America. The cost of using the canal would still be cheaper than the long, hard trip around South America. In 1914, the canal was opened. Ships from all countries could use it. In 1978, President Jimmy Carter signed a bill that gave the country of Panama gradual control of the Panama Canal.

Finally, the United States also sent explorers to the North and South Poles during this period. Robert E. Peary explored the area near the North Pole. This area is called the *Arctic.* Peary claimed he reached 90° N latitude on April 6, 1909. Richard E. Byrd explored Antarctica. He crossed the South Pole on November 28 and 29, 1929. The United States was the first country to succeed in sending explorers to both poles.

The United States had seen many changes during the late 1800s and early 1900s. The country's population increased. The United States acquired new lands including Alaska, Hawaii, and various islands. In addition, the United States oversaw the building of the Panama Canal and sent explorers to both poles. The United States had become a country that was one of the leaders in world affairs.

**Richard E. Byrd**

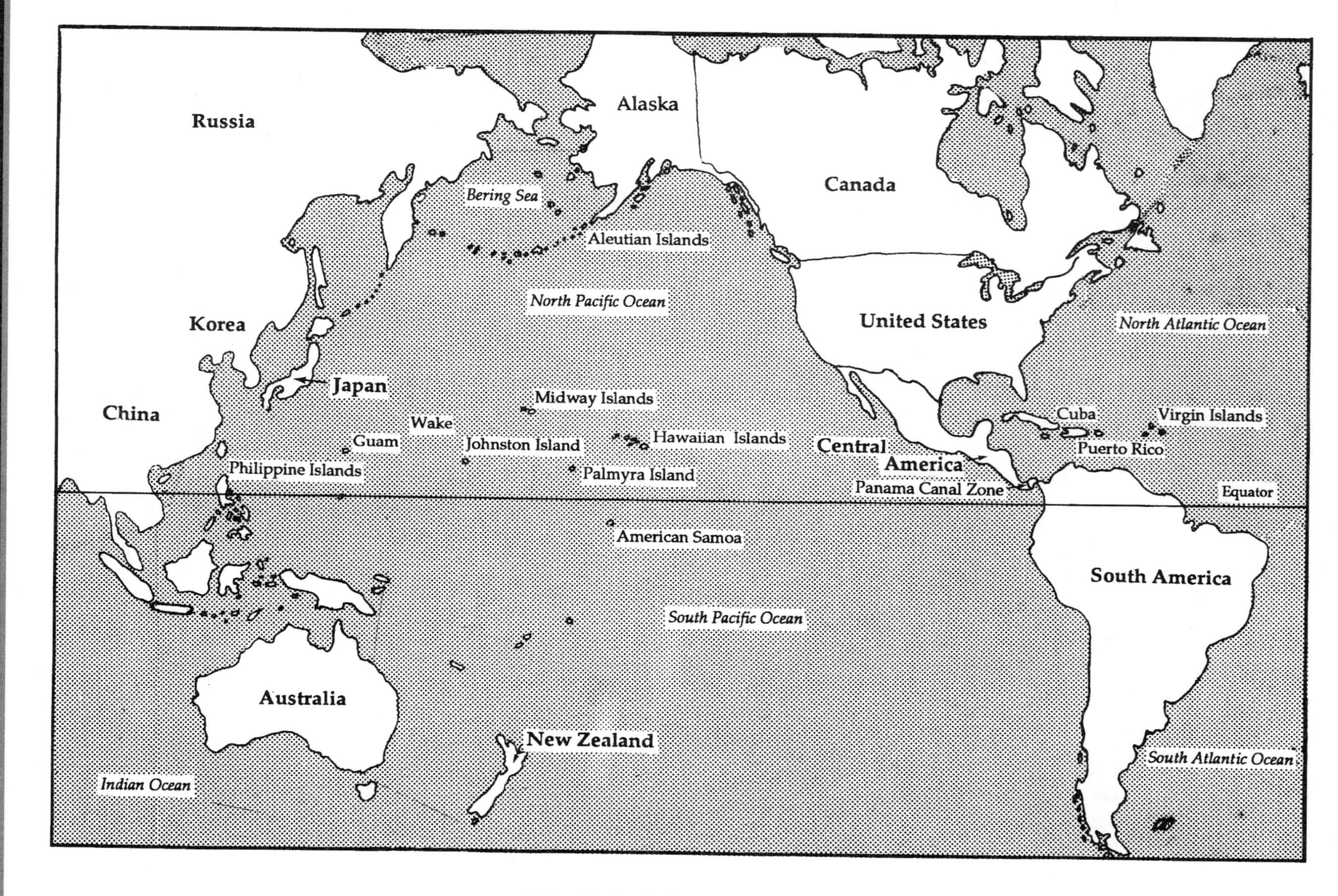


The United States Expands

**American History Time Line**
Turn to the American History Time Line on page 93. On line 8, write "The United States becomes a world power."

## What Did You Find Out?

**A** Study the map on page 54. Then complete the following activities.

1. Locate the United States and Alaska. Color these areas yellow.
2. Circle the following islands:
   - a. Cuba
   - b. Virgin Islands
   - c. Hawaiian Islands
   - d. American Samoa
   - e. Puerto Rico
   - f. Guam
   - g. Philippine Islands
3. Locate the land connecting North and South America. Circle the Panama Canal.

**B** Complete each of the following sentences. Write your answers on the lines provided.

1. The population of the United States in 1890 was nearly ______________ million.
2. ______________, ______________, and ______________ were three very large cities in the United States in 1890.
3. Spain is located on the continent of ______________.
4. The Caribbean Sea is ______________ of the United States.
5. The Pacific Ocean lies ______________ of the United States.
6. Cuba is a major island in the ______________ Sea.
7. The battleship ______________ was blown up in the harbor at ______________, Cuba.
8. President ______________ asked Congress to declare war on ______________ in April 1898.
9. The ______________ War is the name given to the war between the United States and Spain.

UNIT 4

10. What were two outcomes of the Spanish-American War?

a. Cuba became ______________________.

b. Puerto Rico, Guam, and the Philippine Islands became territories of the ______________________.

**C** Write *True* or *False* on the line before each statement.

______________ 1. The United States bought Alaska from Spain.

______________ 2. Hawaii became our fiftieth state in 1959.

______________ 3. The Spanish-American War lasted four years.

______________ 4. The land around the South Pole is called *Antarctica.*

______________ 5. The Arctic was explored by Richard E. Byrd.

______________ 6. Guam and Samoa are located in the Atlantic Ocean.

______________ 7. Hawaii is in the Pacific Ocean.

______________ 8. The Virgin Islands are southeast of the United States.

______________ 9. Alaska is an island.

______________ 10. Cuba became a state in 1959.

**D** Write five important facts about the Panama Canal.

1. ______________________________________________
2. ______________________________________________
3. ______________________________________________
4. ______________________________________________
5. ______________________________________________

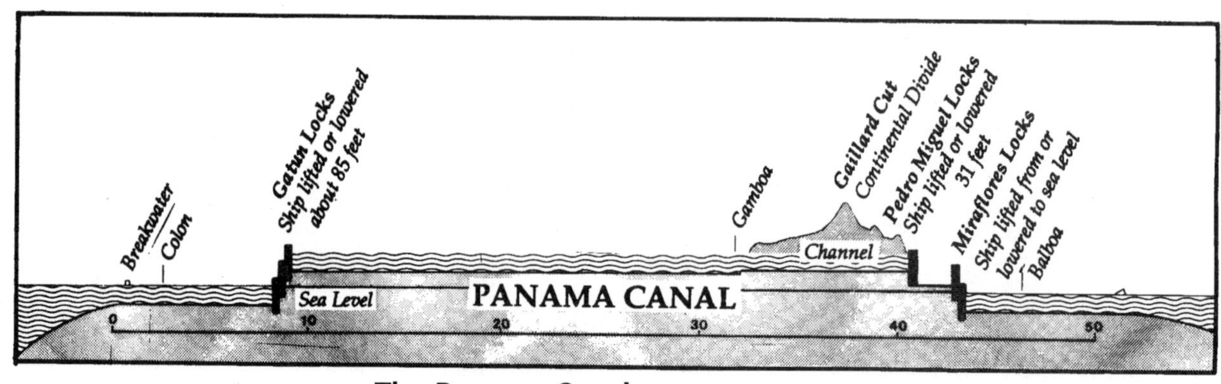


**The Panama Canal**

**E** Read the items listed in the box. Each one is connected with either the North or the South Pole. Write each item on a line in the correct column under either *North Pole* or *South Pole.*

| | |
|---|---|
| 90° N latitude | Robert E. Peary |
| Richard E. Byrd | April 6, 1909 |
| 90° S latitude | November 28 and 29, 1929 |
| Antarctica | Arctic |

| North Pole | South Pole |
|---|---|
| 1. ______________ | 5. ______________ |
| 2. ______________ | 6. ______________ |
| 3. ______________ | 7. ______________ |
| 4. ______________ | 8. ______________ |

**The North and South Poles**

# World War I



Before learning about World War I, you must take a good look at Europe. Europe is a continent mostly in the Eastern Hemisphere. Find the continent of Europe on the map on page 4. Then look at the map on page 61. This map is a close-up of the continent of Europe. Europe is divided into many countries. Read the names of these countries listed on your map.

Almost all of the countries in Europe wanted to become richer, larger, or stronger. Some wanted to become richer by trading more things than other countries. Others wanted to become larger by taking over more land. Little by little, these countries became very jealous of each other.

Before very long, Europe's countries were looking for an excuse to fight. In 1914, this excuse came when Archduke Ferdinand of Austria was killed by a man from Serbia. Soon the fighting began. Austria attacked Serbia. Russia wanted to help Serbia, so it attacked Austria. Then Germany decided to help Austria. Germany also attacked France and Belgium. This made the United Kingdom, or Great Britain, angry, and it began fighting Germany. The Ottoman Empire and Bulgaria decided to help Germany.

When the fighting began, the major countries in Europe were divided into two groups. These groups were called the *Central Powers,* or the countries that supported Austria and Germany, and the *Allies,* or the countries that supported France and Britain. Look again at the map of Europe on page 61. Color the countries that were the Central Powers green. Color the countries that were the Allies yellow.

The Central Powers and the Allies fought for four years. During that time, many bloody battles were fought on land, on the sea, and even in the air. Many new weapons were used for the first time. These new weapons included the airplane, the submarine, and poison gas.

When the fighting began in Europe, most of the people in the United States wanted to stay out of the war. They thought that getting involved in the problems of European countries was not a good thing to do. Instead, the United States should be neutral and not take sides. President Woodrow Wilson also thought that the United States should stay out of the war.

**The Albatros D.V., a World War I Airplane**

The Allies, who were countries friendly to the United States, were in great need of war supplies and food. Business in the United States was booming. Factories were producing as much as they could. American ships took supplies to the Allies. Everyone believed that the Allies would win and that the war would end soon.

Germany, however, began sinking American supply ships. Their submarines were able to destroy unarmed ships easily. President Wilson and the people of the United States believed that international trade should not be attacked. All countries should have the right to trade. The seas should be neutral. President Wilson asked Germany to stop its submarine attacks, but the attacks continued.

The war that had begun in August of 1914 continued with no interest in compromise by either side. President Wilson had no choice. On April 6, 1917, the United States declared war against the Central Powers of Europe. Soon American soldiers were on their way to fight in Europe. They were led by General John Pershing.

More than two million American soldiers were sent to Europe. The American navy protected ships from German submarine attacks. The war was not going very well for the Central Powers. After losing many big battles, Germany and the other Central Powers surrendered. The war ended on November 11, 1918. The time was 11 o'clock on the eleventh day of the eleventh month. For many years, this date was called *Armistice Day.* In 1954, the name was changed to Veterans Day to honor all American soldiers who have fought for their country.

World War I was over. It had lasted about four years, from 1914 to 1918. During that time, over seven million soldiers were killed and several million were wounded. The continent of Europe was in ruins.

**World War I German Soldier**

| Soldiers Killed | World War I Country |
|---|---|
| 116,516 | United States |
| 1,700,000 | Russia |
| 1,773,000 | Germany |
| 1,385,000 | France |
| 908,400 | British Empire |
| 1,200,000 | Austria-Hungary |
| 7,082,916 | **Total** |

**American History Time Line**
Turn to the American History Time Line on page 93. On line 9, write "The United States enters World War I."

**Famous Americans**
As a child, this person was not able to begin school until he was nine years old. He had a hard time learning because his eyes were very weak. However, he studied very hard and, as a young man, became a lawyer. Later, he began studying and teaching about government in several colleges.

In 1910, he became the governor of New Jersey. He was very successful and went on to be elected President of the United States two times. You know him because he was the President of our country during World War I.

Can you name this famous American President? Write his name on the line under his picture.

______________________

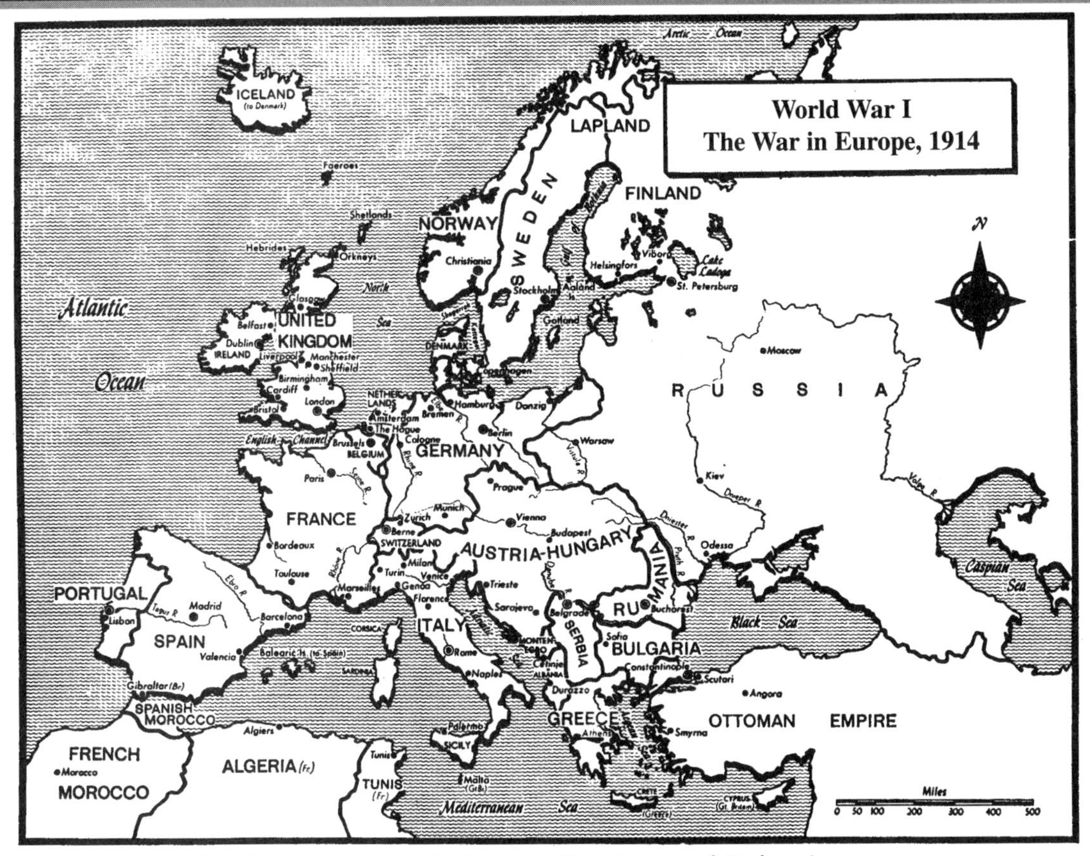


**Central Powers:** Austria, Germany, the Ottoman Empire, and Bulgaria
**Allies:** Russia, France, Belgium, the United Kingdom, and the United States (not shown)

## What Did You Find Out?

**A** Write *True* or *False* on the line before each statement.

______ 1. World War I was fought on the continent of Europe.

______ 2. World War I began in 1918.

______ 3. The king of Austria was killed by a man from Serbia.

______ 4. Germany, Bulgaria, Austria, and the Ottoman Empire were all Central Powers.

______ 5. The United States began fighting because Germany would not stop sinking our ships.

______ 6. The United States entered World War I in 1915.

______ 7. Woodrow Wilson was the leader of the American army in Europe.

______ 8. November 11 is called *Memorial Day.*

______ 9. World War I lasted a total of three years.

______ 10. The Allies were countries friendly to the United States.

UNIT 4

**B** Write the answer to each of the following questions.

1. Who was President of the United States during this time in history?

_______________________________________________

2. Who was the leader of the American army in Europe?

_______________________________________________

3. How many soldiers were killed during World War I?

_______________________________________________

4. Look at the chart on page 60. Which two countries lost the most soldiers?

_______________________________________________

5. What were two weapons used for the first time in this war?

_______________________________________________

**C** Look at the map on page 61. Then complete the following activities.

1. This map shows the countries on the continent of ____________.
2. England is a country on an island in the ____________ Ocean.
3. The United States joined the Allied countries of Russia, France, Belgium, and ____________.
4. Germany, Austria, Bulgaria, and ____________ were Central Powers.
5. Most of Italy is in the ____________ Sea.
6. Bulgaria is located between ____________ and the Black Sea.
7. The country across the English Channel from England is ____________.
8. Austria-Hungary was a large country located ____________ of Serbia.
9. Italy bordered one Central Power, ____________, and one Allied country, ____________.
10. What three Allied countries bordered Germany?
    a. ______________________________
    b. ______________________________
    c. ______________________________

# After World War I





After World War I, many important things happened in Europe and in the United States. If you were alive during this time in history, you would have read about these things in newspaper stories.

You will learn about the years after World War I by reading the new stories in this lesson. One of the important news stories concerned the plans of President Wilson.

SECURITY E and TRUST CO.

WEATHER AND SUMMARY

LOCAL FORECAST FOR TODAY.

Rain or Snow.

16 AMERICANS SLAIN BY MEXICANS

MR. GRASTY GOES TO THE TIMES

Will Succeed Charles W. Knapp As Treasurer.

BULL MOOSE EXTENDS OLIVE BRANCH TO G.

To Hold National Convention Chicago At Same Time As Older Party's.

HOPE TO AGREE ON NOMINEE

## WILSON HAS PLANS FOR PEACE

Paris, France—Today President Woodrow Wilson met again with the leaders of the European countries. During this meeting, he told the leaders about his plan for stopping any wars from happening again.

### The Plan

Wilson asked all countries to join together in one group. This group would listen to the problems and troubles between countries. It would try to settle these problems peaceably.

President Wilson called this group of countries the *League of Nations*.

UNIT 4

President Wilson worked very hard. Soon the League of Nations was set up. At first, 42 countries decided to join the League of Nations. Later others joined. The United States, however, did not join. Our country did not want to get directly involved in Europe's problems again.

For a short time, the League of Nations did many good things. However, most countries were not yet ready to settle all of their problems without fighting. Soon the League of Nations broke up. In the United States, Americans did not pay much attention to the league. The next story tells why.

## AMERICANS ENJOY BOOM YEARS

Most Americans are now enjoying life in a very rich country. People are earning good wages. Our factories are making more products to buy.

Today thousands of Americans own new cars. New homes are being built every day. Americans have more time for leisure activities including going to see movies and watching sports. Machines are making our lives easier than ever before.

ALKER AND SHADE MAKING FEW CLAIMS BEFORE BOUT

By Fair Play

NEW YORK, Sept. 18—Concerning the Walker-Shade battle on Monday night in New York is it noticeable that very little in the way of pre-battle statements has been issued from er camp. This because both men are putting in the hardest licks heir young lives to make weight and be in the pink of condition n the bell sends them into action.

CHURCH NINES MEET TOMORROW FOR FLAG

The baseball nines of the Calvary Lutheran Church and the Boundary M. E. will clash tomorrow for the supremacy of the division A of the Baltimore Federation Sunday-School League at Herring Run.

Meetings.

ACHES CLEAN SPORT

ta Cops Pennant Southern League

Champs To Cla

Faith Tackles Sa

New Fall H

$7.00

Emphasizing the very broad, semi-soft toe, rolled-edge extension heel and heavy rope stitching around sole.

Outstanding Quality & St

A most complete showing of best of all shap please every man. Large variety of the season's colors.

STETSON HATS, $8

MALLOR HATS, $5-

MELVIN

COLLEGIA

Before long the "good times" got out of control. Many Americans bought expensive things. They paid just a little for the goods and promised to pay the rest later. This type of buying is called *using credit.* In other words, Americans were spending more money than they had. Soon many people could not pay for all of the items they had bought.

Factories and farmers also helped the "good times" get out of hand. Factories were producing more than they could sell. Farmers planted more crops than they could sell. Few rules were placed on how the banks and stock markets had to operate.

All of these excesses soon led to a very sad story.

MARKET STAMPEDE

**AMERICANS FACE A DEPRESSION**

Millions of American people are not able to buy any more goods. Factories that make these goods will have to close.

Thousands of workers will lose their jobs. Because these workers will not be making a salary, they will not be able to pay for things they have bought. Homes, cars, boats, and furniture might be taken away from them.

Many Americans will not have enough money for necessities. They might not be able to buy food or to pay rent.

In a very short time, over 13 million Americans were out of work. Many people lost their homes, businesses, and farms. They could not pay the money they owed. This was the start of a long, hard time in our country.

Soon the American people began looking for a strong President to help lead our country back to better times. In 1932, they chose Franklin D. Roosevelt (F.D.R.). He had a plan for helping the United States become strong and rich again. Our next news story describes Roosevelt's plan, the New Deal.

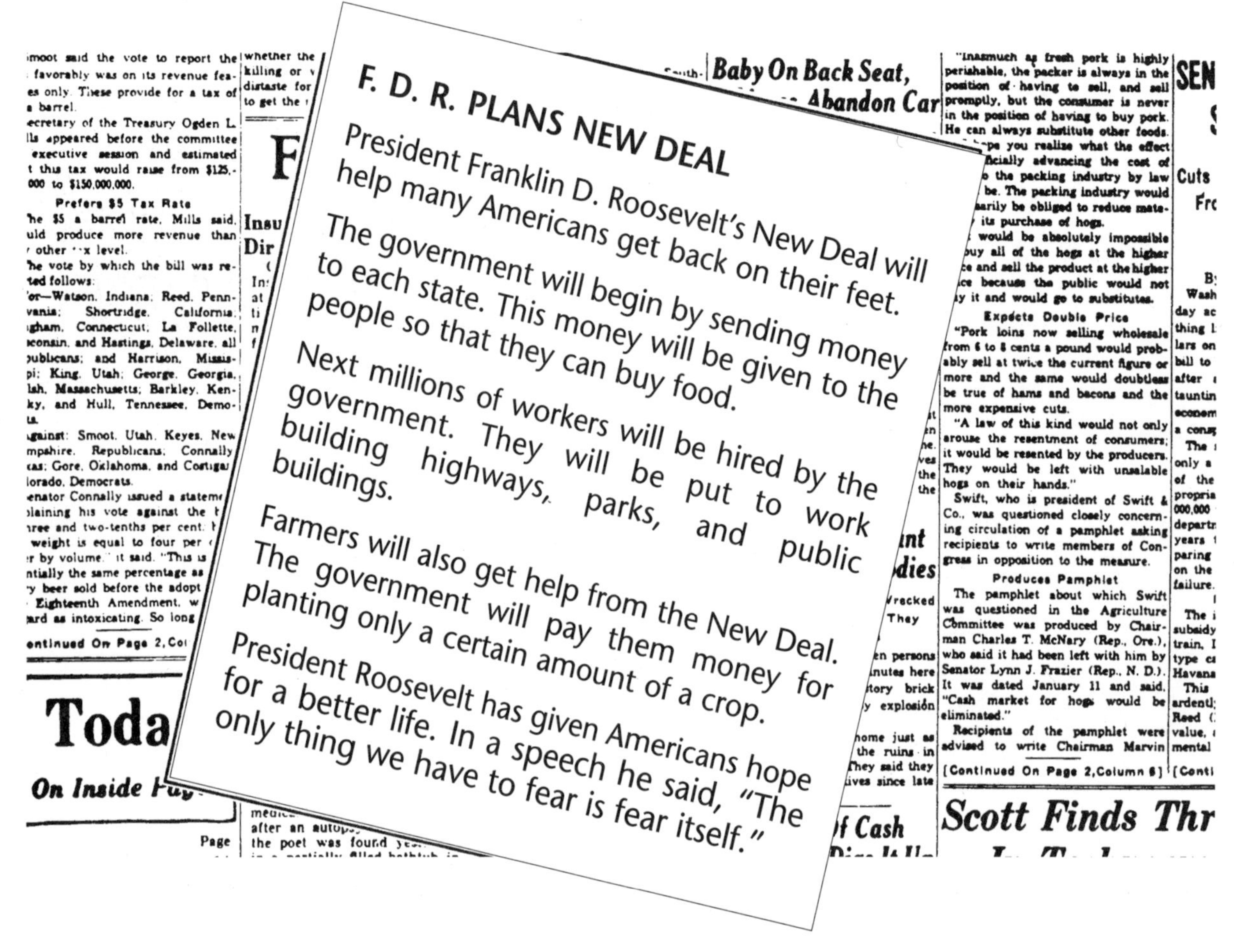

## F. D. R. PLANS NEW DEAL

President Franklin D. Roosevelt's New Deal will help many Americans get back on their feet.

The government will begin by sending money to each state. This money will be given to the people so that they can buy food.

Next millions of workers will be hired by the government. They will be put to work building highways, parks, and public buildings.

Farmers will also get help from the New Deal. The government will pay them money for planting only a certain amount of a crop.

President Roosevelt has given Americans hope for a better life. In a speech he said, "The only thing we have to fear is fear itself."

President Roosevelt did many things to help Americans. He helped pass laws that protected workers against losing their jobs or working for low pay. He also worked on laws that would control business and help prevent another depression. Perhaps his most famous law is the Social Security Act. Today this law is still helping older and retired people, poor children, and the disabled.

President Roosevelt's New Deal plans helped the United States become a little stronger. However, even after ten years of trying to get back to better times, many people still had no jobs. No one will ever know whether or not Roosevelt's plan would have ended the depression. Before the New Deal programs had proven themselves, our country once again had to get ready for war.

**Famous Americans**

He became the thirty-second President of the United States. Earlier in life he had contacted polio, a viral disease, which left him unable to walk. However, this famous American was a lawyer, New York state senator, and assistant secretary of the navy as well as President.

In 1932 he was elected President. He stayed in the President's office for over 12 years. That is the most time that any one person has ever been President of our country. He is best known for his New Deal plans.

Write the name of this man on the line under his picture.

____________________________________

## What Did You Find Out?

**A** Many things happened during the years after World War I. Put these events in their correct order by writing 1, 2, 3, etc., on the lines below.

______ Franklin Roosevelt helps Americans with his New Deal.

______ President Wilson asks countries to form a League of Nations.

______ World War I ends.

______ Americans enjoy boom years.

______ The United States faces a depression.

UNIT 4

**B** President Roosevelt gave the American people hope. Reread the newspaper story on page 66. What did Roosevelt say?

______________________________________________

**C** Read each sentence in the box below. Then write each one in the chart under the correct heading: *Boom Years* or *Depression Years.*

| | |
|---|---|
| People lose homes, farms, and cars. | Workers need food and money. |
| People work long hours. | Wages are low. |
| Factories are closed. | Wages are high. |
| People buy expensive goods. | Many workers lose jobs. |
| Most people have jobs. | Factories make many things. |

| **Boom Years** | **Depression Years** |
|---|---|
| 1. ______________ | 6. ______________ |
| 2. ______________ | 7. ______________ |
| 3. ______________ | 8. ______________ |
| 4. ______________ | 9. ______________ |
| 5. ______________ | 10. ______________ |

**D** Underline the phrase that best completes each statement.

1. The League of Nations did not work because
   - **a.** the United States joined.
   - **b.** only a few countries joined.
   - **c.** the countries were not ready to solve all of their problems peaceably.
2. The United States did not join the League of Nations because
   - **a.** only Europe's countries could join.
   - **b.** it did not want to get directly involved in Europe's problems again.
   - **c.** President Wilson did not think we should join.
3. The Social Security Act
   - **a.** is still helping people today.
   - **b.** was the cause of the depression.
   - **c.** protects workers against losing their jobs.
4. All of these things helped cause the Great Depression except one.
   - **a.** Americans were spending more money than they had.
   - **b.** Factories made more things than they could sell.
   - **c.** Americans saved too much of their money.

# World War II





During World War I, most of the continent of Europe was ruined. Farms, factories, and towns had been torn apart or burned. Life was very hard for the people in many of Europe's countries. Soon these people began looking for strong leaders. They hoped that these leaders would help their countries get back to better times.

In Italy, the people decided to follow Benito Mussolini. At first, Mussolini helped make Italy a strong country. He did many good things for the people. Then, little by little, he took over control of the whole country. Soon he made all the laws and ran the government by himself. A person who does this is called a *dictator.* The people who followed Mussolini were called *Fascists.* Mussolini and the Fascists planned to make Italy a much larger and stronger country by taking over other countries.

Find Italy on the map on page 70. Color it red.

A few years later, the people in Germany decided to follow Adolf Hitler. By promising to make Germany a strong, rich country again, he soon became a dictator. His followers were called *Nazis.* After he took control of the government, Hitler began building a strong army, navy, and air force. The Nazis were also planning to take over other countries.

Find Germany on the map on page 70. Color it red.

Germany and Italy joined with the country of Japan. Japan is an island country off the coast of Asia. Germany, Italy, and Japan had a common goal: each wanted to become larger and stronger. When the fighting began, these countries were called the *Axis Powers.*

Find Japan on the map on page 72. Color it red.

Many countries all over the world began to fear what the Axis Powers might do. In 1931, the trouble began when Japan took over the Chinese province of Manchuria. Four years later, Italy took over Ethiopia. This country is located on the continent of Africa. Japan attacked China in 1937. The next year, Germany took over Austria and a part of Czechoslovakia. Germany also took over Poland in 1939. Great Britain and France then declared war against Germany. The war in Europe had begun. The following year, Germany took over Denmark, Norway, the Netherlands, Belgium, and France. Then it attacked Greece. In 1940, Germany also attacked Great Britain and in 1941 Russia.

Find England (Great Britain) and France on this map. Color them green.

Look at the maps on this page and on page 72. Find all of the countries that were attacked by the Axis Powers.

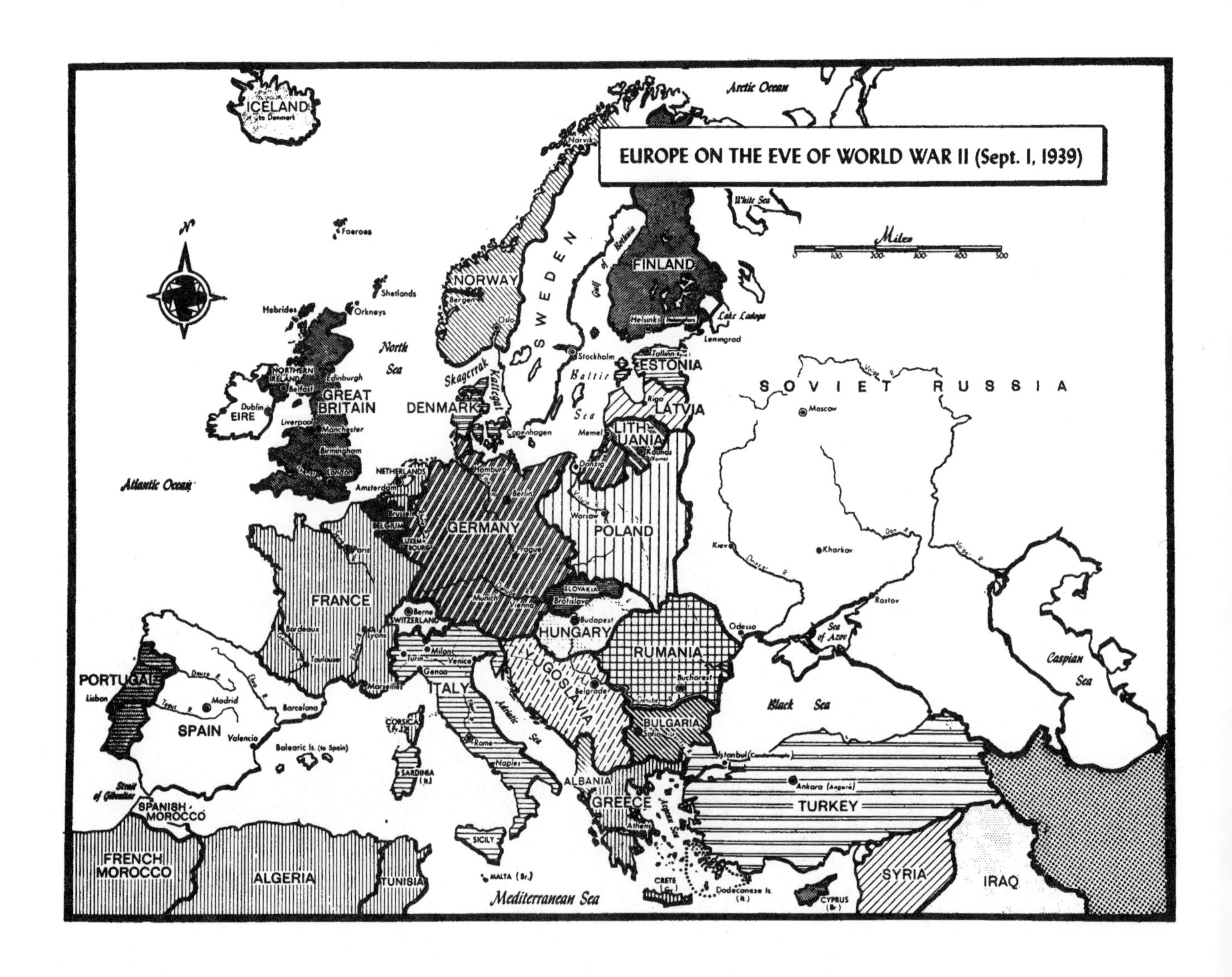

Most of the people of the United States did not want to get involved in the war in Europe. The Great Depression and loss of jobs in the 1930s had caused very hard times for Americans. At this time, factories were just beginning to start up again. Our country wanted to remain neutral, or not take sides. The United States sent supplies to European countries and also to China. The Japanese did not want the United States to help China. They also did not want the United States to stop the Japanese military takeover of Pacific islands.

On December 7, 1941, Japan attacked American ships and airfields at Pearl Harbor in Hawaii. When the smoke cleared, over 2,400 Americans had been killed, and 19 warships were either sunk or badly damaged. The bombing of Pearl Harbor brought the United States into World War II.

Find Hawaii on the map on page 72. Circle the Hawaiian Islands in green.

On December 8, 1941, President Roosevelt asked Congress to declare war on Japan. Three days later, Germany and Italy declared war on the United States. As a result, our country had to fight on two fronts: against Germany and Italy in both Europe and Africa and against Japan in the Pacific region.

The United States, England, and France fought together against the Axis Powers. These three countries were called the *Allies.*

Before too long, the American army, navy, and air force were ready for battle. General Dwight Eisenhower was the leader of our soldiers in Europe and Africa. Most of the battles fought on these two continents were on land. At the same time, Admiral William F. Halsey was put in charge of the fighting in the Pacific Ocean. Most of the fighting there was done on the sea. Many long, bloody battles were fought on both fronts.

**The B-24 Liberator**
**A World War II Airplane**

After the United States began fighting, Hitler and the Nazis knew that they would never be able to conquer the world as they had planned. On May 7, 1945, the war in Europe ended. Mussolini was captured and killed. Hitler killed himself.

The United States wanted to end the war in the Pacific quickly. In 1945, the United States dropped one atomic bomb on the Japanese city of Hiroshima and a second bomb on the city of Nagasaki. Both cities were in ruins. Thousands of people were killed. Thousands more were ill from radiation sickness as a result of the blast. Five days after the bombing of Nagasaki, on August 14, 1945, Japan surrendered.

UNIT 5

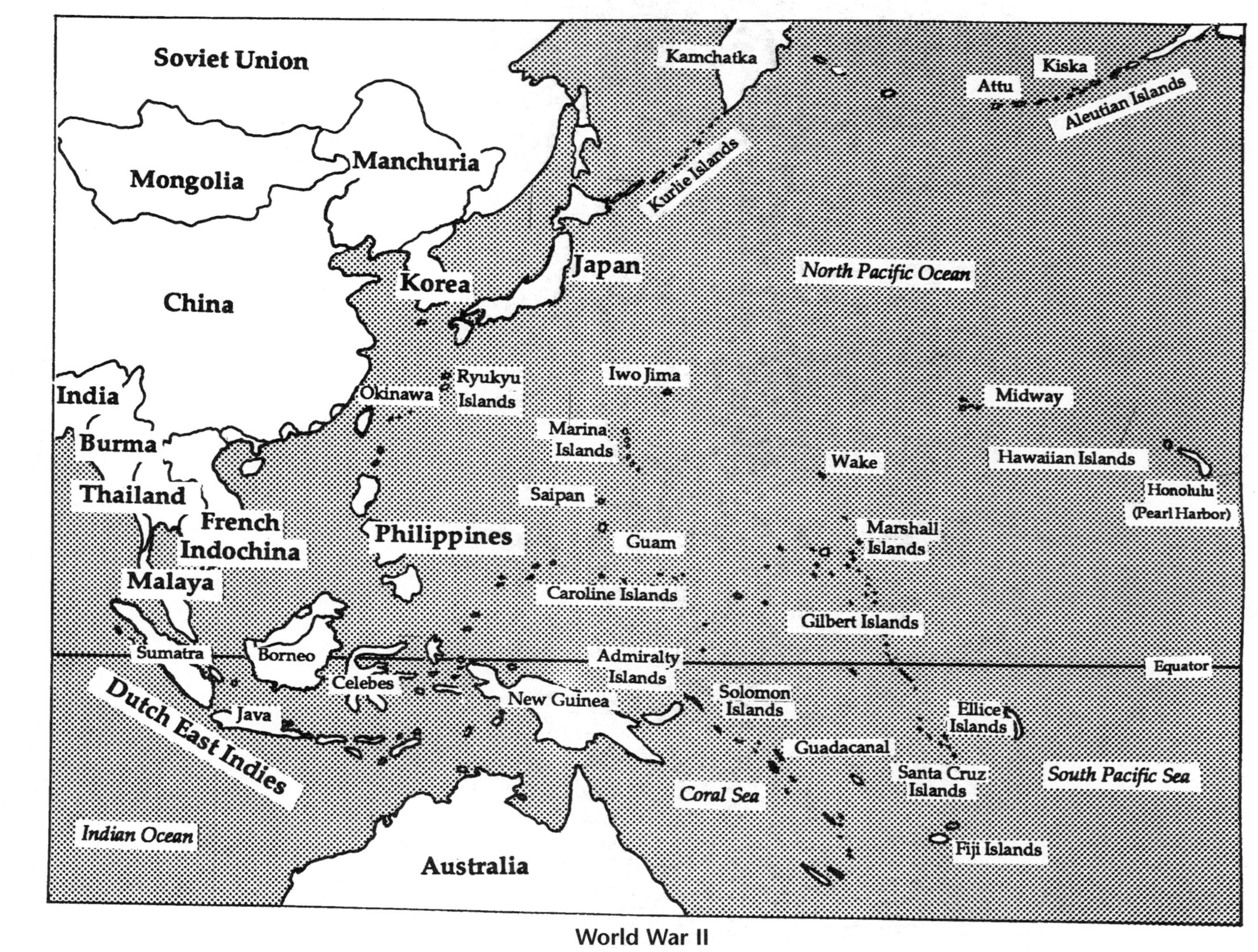


World War II
The War in the Pacific, 1941–1945

World War II was the biggest and most costly war ever fought. About 17 million people were killed, and about 34 million were badly hurt. After the war, the people in many countries suffered from hunger, cold, and disease. The damage in many cities and countries was extensive.

**American History Time Line**
Turn to your American History Time Line on page 93. On line 10, write "The United States fights in World War II."

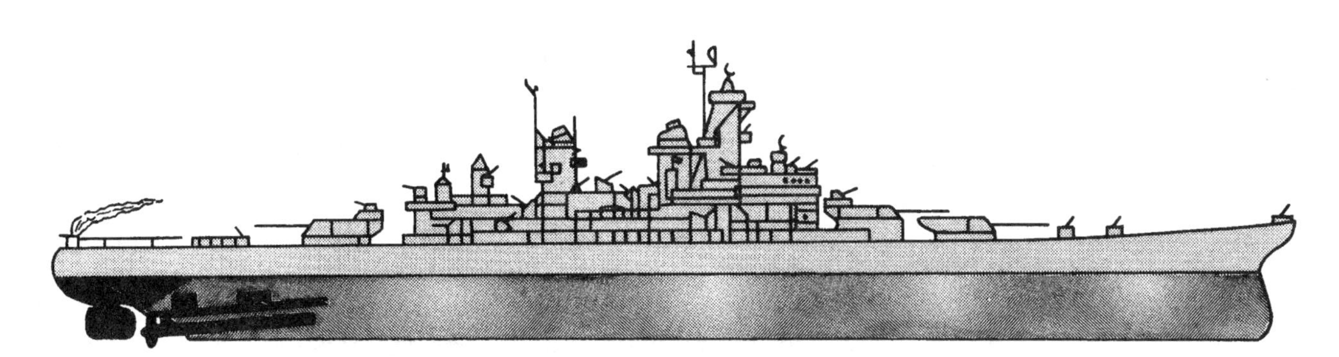

**A World War II Battleship**

## What Did You Find Out?

**A** During World War II, countries again were divided into two groups. Write each of the countries below under its correct group, the *Axis Powers* or the *Allies.*

| Great Britain | Germany | France |
|---|---|---|
| Italy | Japan | United States |

| Axis Powers | Allies |
|---|---|
| 1. ______________________ | 4. ______________________ |
| 2. ______________________ | 5. ______________________ |
| 3. ______________________ | 6. ______________________ |

UNIT 5

**B** Put these sentences about World War II in the proper order. Place 1, 2, 3, etc., on the lines provided.

_____ The war in the Pacific ends.

_____ Germany, Italy, and Japan attack other countries.

_____ Great Britain and France declare war against Germany.

_____ The war in Europe ends.

_____ The United States declares war.

_____ Pearl Harbor is attacked.

**C** Write the answers to the following questions.

1. Who was the leader of Italy? ____________________
2. What were his followers called? ____________________
3. Who was the leader of Germany? ____________________
4. What were his followers called? ____________________
5. What kind of bomb was used in Japan? ____________________
6. What is the name given to a person who runs a government alone? ____________________
7. Who led the American navy in the Pacific? ____________________
8. Who led the American army in Europe? ____________________

**D** Match the places in column 1 with the correct statement in column 2.

| | Column 1 | Column 2 |
|---|---|---|
| _____ | 1. Italy | a. attacked China in 1937. |
| _____ | 2. Manchuria | b. declared war on Germany in 1939. |
| _____ | 3. Japan | c. was attacked by the Japanese in 1941. |
| _____ | 4. Great Britain and France | d. took over Poland. |
| _____ | 5. Hiroshima | e. was led by Mussolini. |
| _____ | 6. Ethiopia | f. was a Chinese province. |
| _____ | 7. Nagasaki | g. is located on the continent of Africa. |
| _____ | 8. Germany | h. was hit by the first atomic bomb. |
| _____ | 9. Pearl Harbor | i. joined the Allies. |
| _____ | 10. The United States | j. was hit by the second atomic bomb. |

**E** World War II lasted for many years. Write the correct dates for each of the events below.

_______________ 1. In what year did Japan take over the Chinese province of Manchuria?

_______________ 2. In what year did England and France declare war?

_______________ 3. Give the date on which Pearl Harbor was attacked.

_______________ 4. Give the date on which Roosevelt asked the United States Congress to declare war on Japan.

_______________ 5. During what years was World War II fought in Europe?

_______________ 6. Give the date on which Japan surrendered.

**F** Define each of the following terms. Use complete sentences.

1. Neutral _______________
2. Allies _______________
3. Depression _______________
4. Dictator _______________
5. Atomic bomb _______________

**Mushroom Cloud Explosion from Atomic Bomb**

U N I T 5

# After World War II



After World War II, the continent of Europe was again in ruins. Factories, farms, and towns had been torn apart or burned. Homes had been destroyed. The people in Europe did not have enough food. They did not have warm clothes. Many were very sick. Even though war had ended, many problems remained.

The United States did much to help the people of Europe. Help given by one country to another is called *foreign aid.* There are three kinds of foreign aid: economic aid, political aid, and military aid.

American ships and airplanes took food, medicine, and clothes to Europe. Our government also sent money. This money was used to build new factories, towns, farms, and homes. This type of aid is called *economic aid.*

The United States also helped many European countries set up new governments. During the war, England, France, and the United States drove the German army out of many countries. Now they were trying to help the countries rebuild their governments. This type of aid is called *political aid.*

Look at the map below. Locate the countries of Western Europe. All are shaded on your map. Color them blue.

The thick black line on your map divides Eastern and Western Europe. This line was called the *Iron Curtain.* Locate the countries of Eastern Europe on your map. These countries are east of the Iron Curtain. Color them red.

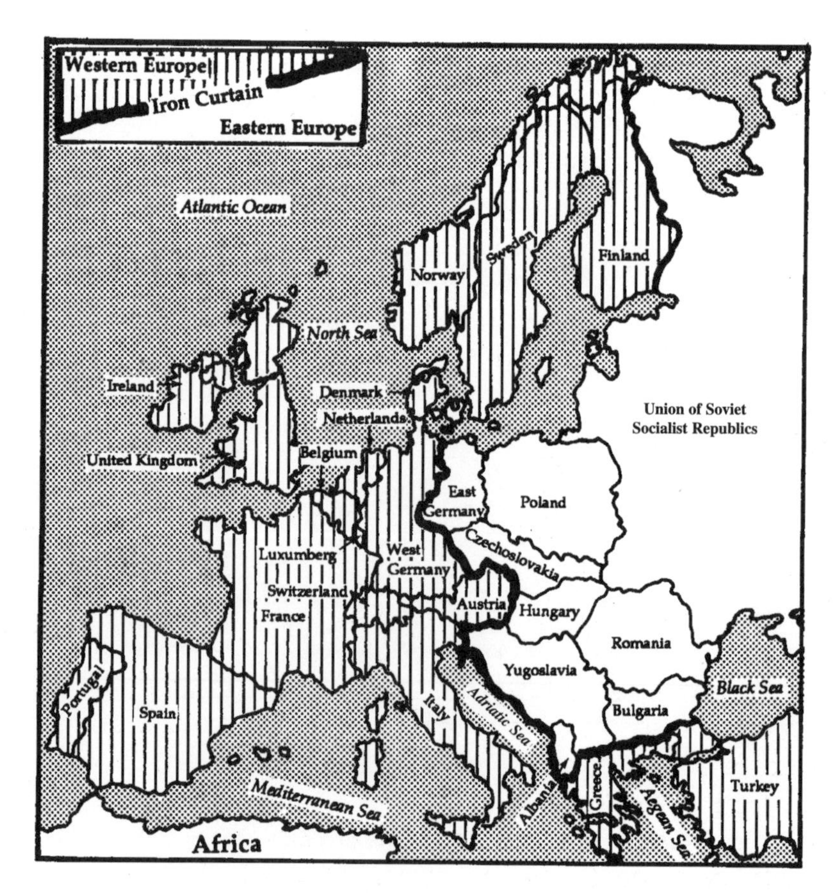


The Iron Curtain

The Soviet Union set several Eastern European countries free from German rule during the war. After the war, the Soviet Union did not want to give those countries up. The leader of the Soviet Union was Joseph Stalin. Stalin made sure that the countries in Eastern Europe set up Communist governments just like the Soviet Union's.

Communism is a system of government in which the people do not have basic freedoms. For example, speech, religion, voting, private business, and travel are either not permitted or severely limited. Most of the land, farms, and factories are owned and controlled by the government. People have little choice of candidates in elections. They can vote only for members of the Communist Party. No one can oppose or vote against these leaders.

The people have to do whatever the government wants. In countries where communism still exists, a few people hold all of the power.

The United States did not feel that some of these countries in Eastern Europe had a fair chance to choose the kind of governments they really wanted. The United States promised to give aid to any country that might be taken over by communism.

Since World War II, the United States has given help to many countries all over the world. For example, West Germany, Greece, France, and Italy have received much economic and political aid. Other countries, like South Korea, have been given soldiers, guns, and planes to help them fight communism. This type of aid is called *military aid.*

Vietnam is another country that the United States tried to help. This Asian country was divided into two parts, North Vietnam and South Vietnam. North Vietnam had a Communist government that wanted to take over South Vietnam. The United States tried to help South Vietnam with economic, political, and military aid. In 1961, our country began sending American soldiers there. Over the next fourteen years, over 58,000 American soldiers died in Vietnam. Soon many Americans began to feel that our country had done enough. Young Americans felt that the war was not right and refused to fight. Finally, in 1973, a peace treaty was signed. Two years later, however, the army of North Vietnam again attacked South Vietnam and conquered it. The country of Vietnam is now a Communist nation.

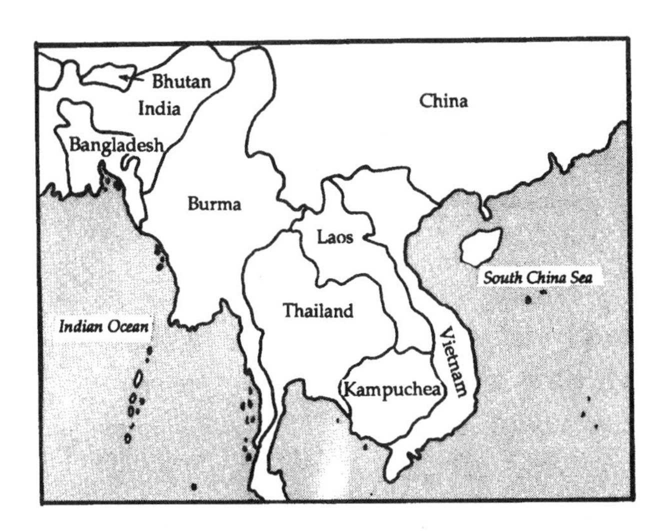


**Vietnam**

UNIT 5

For a long time, the strongest Communist country was the Soviet Union. For many years after World War II, the Soviet Union and the United States were not friendly. Neither country trusted the other. During this time, the Soviet Union and its ally China tried to spread communism. The United States opposed the spread of communism. This conflict was called the *Cold War.* The war was called "cold" because it involved words and attitudes more often than actual fighting. Nevertheless, tensions ran very high. The United States and the Soviet Union were very strong countries. Both had many powerful weapons. For many years, each country tried to build arms faster than the other. This arms race cost both countries much money.

Atomic bombs are the most powerful weapons of all. The United States and the Soviet Union had many atomic bombs. These bombs are so powerful that it would take only a few of them to destroy a whole country. If enough atomic bombs were used, the entire world might be destroyed.

Over the years, however, both the United States and the Soviet Union began to work to end the arms race. In the 1980s, the cold war was ending. The United States and the Soviet Union agreed to stop building new atomic bombs. They also agreed to take apart many weapons that were already built. Taking apart or reducing existing weapons is called *disarmament.*

The United States and the Soviet Union had many meetings about arms. These meetings were called the *Strategic Arms Limitations Talks* (SALT). These SALT meetings did much to help control the spread of atomic bombs and other powerful weapons near the end of the Cold War.

In the late 1980s and early 1990s, the Soviet Union collapsed, and many Eastern European nations gained their independence. The United States worked closely with these nations to help them become more democratic.

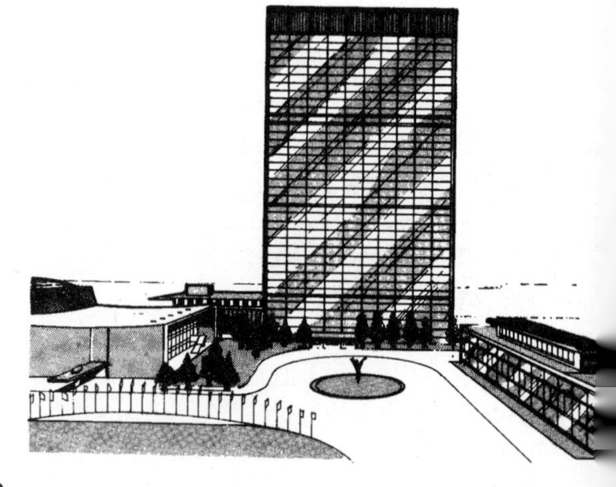

**The United Nations Building**

Since World War II, many of the world's nations have been working to keep peace through the United Nations. The United Nations is much like the League of Nations that was set up after World War I. The United States did not join the League of Nations, but our country is a member of the United Nations. Representatives from countries all over the world meet together in one group. This group listens to the differences between countries and tries to find a fair answer or solution.

So far, the United Nations has been able to settle many problems between nations. It has also sent food, medicine, doctors, farmers, and teachers to nations that need aid.

## What Did You Find Out?

**A** Write *True* or *False* on the line before each statement.

_______________ 1. After World War II, Europe was again in ruins.

_______________ 2. The United States helped countries in Western Europe to set up new governments.

_______________ 3. The Soviet Union did not want to give up the countries in Eastern Europe.

_______________ 4. Providing money for factories is an example of military aid.

_______________ 5. The leader of the Soviet Union after World War II was Stalin.

_______________ 6. The Soviet Union became stronger in the late 1980s.

_______________ 7. Taking apart arms is called an *arms race.*

_______________ 8. The most powerful weapons of all are atomic bombs.

_______________ 9. Countries are now trying to keep peace by working together in the League of Nations.

**B** Read the words listed in the box below. Choose the word or phrase that completes each statement correctly. Write these words on the lines provided.

| | | |
|---|---|---|
| Cold | Iron | Soviet Union |
| Eastern | SALT | Communist |

1. After World War II, Europe was divided into Western Europe and _______________ Europe.
2. The countries in Eastern Europe set up _______________ governments.
3. The _______________ Curtain was a line that divided Eastern and Western Europe.
4. The strongest Communist country after World War II was the _______________.
5. A war without fighting is called a _______________ War.
6. _______________ meetings have done much to help control the spread of atomic bombs and other powerful weapons.

**C** Help given by one country to another is called *foreign aid.* The three kinds of foreign aid are listed below. Match each type of aid in column 1 with its meaning in column 2.

| | Column 1 | Column 2 |
|---|---|---|
| _____ | 1. Economic aid | a. help in setting up a government |
| _____ | 2. Political aid | b. guns, bombs, and soldiers |
| _____ | 3. Military aid | c. food, medicine, and money |

UNIT 5

**D** Define each of the following words. Use complete sentences.

1. Communism

______________________________

2. Iron Curtain

______________________________

3. Soviet Union

______________________________

4. Cold War

______________________________

5. United Nations

______________________________

6. Disarmament

______________________________

**American History Time Line**
Use your American History Time Line on page 93. Put the sentences below in their proper order. Write 1, 2, 3, etc., on the lines provided.

_____ The English settle in Jamestown.

_____ Europeans begin exploring the Americas.

_____ World War II takes place.

_____ The thirteen colonies become free after the Revolutionary War.

_____ The United States and the Soviet Union engage in a cold war.

_____ The Civil War takes place.

_____ The United States becomes a world power.

_____ Only Indians live in the Americas.

_____ World War I takes place.

# The Presidency: 1960 to the Present





The United States has lasted for over two hundred years so far. During this time, our government had to be strong enough to fight for freedom, face the hard times of depression, and fight in two world wars. From 1960 to the present, our country has had to be concerned with problems, seek solutions, and rejoice in moments of success. Many Presidents have been involved in the events of these years.

John F. Kennedy was elected to the presidency in 1960. He is best known for working to bring about improvements in civil rights, in antipoverty proposals, and in tax reform laws. His speeches and dashing manner won popular support. However, political opponents worked against many of his legislative ideas. In October 1962, Kennedy announced that the United States had proof that the Soviet Union was building missile sites in Cuba. He ordered a blockade of Cuba until the Soviet Union agreed to remove all offensive weapons from the island. Kennedy's firm stand succeeded. The crisis passed. Americans had won a remarkable and yet peaceful victory.

On November 22, 1963, John F. Kennedy was shot and killed by Lee Harvey Oswald in Dallas, Texas. This assassination was a shock to the nation. In many countries, the death of a President might mean the end of that country's government. But this did not happen in the United States. Several hours after President Kennedy was shot, the United States had a new President. Our government was able to continue functioning.

**John F. Kennedy**

**Lyndon B. Johnson**

This new President was Lyndon B. Johnson. President Johnson continued the civil rights work begun by Kennedy. He wanted to help the poor and to lower taxes. His program was called the *Great Society.* Many Americans approved of Johnson's programs at home, but they disapproved of his policies in Vietnam.

During the time that Johnson was President, our government was sending more and more soldiers to Vietnam. Many Americans came to feel that our government had done enough for that country. Some young people would not fight in Vietnam. All over the United States, people were saying that our government and its leaders were wrong in becoming so involved in the conflicts in another country. Many angry speeches were made against our government and its leaders. Pressure was brought upon the government to withdraw American troops from Vietnam. It was a difficult time for the President.

President Johnson decided not to run for re-election. In 1968, the American people elected a new president, Richard M. Nixon. This President slowly brought home many of our soldiers from Vietnam. After he was elected for a second time, he and one of his aides, Secretary of State Henry Kissinger, ended the war in Vietnam by helping write a peace treaty.

**Richard M. Nixon**

President Nixon also helped our country work better with other countries, such as China and the Soviet Union. Soon our government was working more closely with the Soviet Union. President Nixon was also invited to visit China. This visit to China was the first one ever made by an American President.

Soon after Nixon began his second term, however, his Vice President was accused of tax evasion and of taking part in a bribery scandal. Vice President Spiro T. Agnew resigned and pleaded "no contest" to the charges. According to the Twenty-fifth Amendment to the Constitution, when a Vice President leaves office in the middle of a term, the President names a new Vice President. Congress must approve the new Vice President before he or she takes office. Nixon chose Gerald R. Ford to become his new Vice President.

**Gerald R. Ford**

Later, the government had to face even bigger problems. The American people began to learn that many of President Nixon's other aides and assistants—and perhaps even the President himself—had broken many laws. Americans first learned about this scandal when some burglars were caught breaking into an office in the Watergate building in 1972. They were caught tampering with the telephones. These telephones were used by the Democrats, who were running their election campaign against Nixon from offices in the building. It was discovered that the burglars worked for some of Nixon's closest aides.

As time went by, more and more was learned about broken laws and attempts made to keep the American people from finding out about the Watergate scandal.

Some members of Congress believed that Nixon should be impeached, or accused of a crime, because of his part in the Watergate affair. If a President were found guilty of a crime, he could be removed from office. To avoid impeachment, President Nixon decided to resign in August of 1974. His Vice President, Gerald R. Ford, became the new President. For the first time, the United States had a President who was never elected by the people as either Vice President or President.

During Ford's term of office, the United States celebrated its bicentennial on July 4, 1976. A bicentennial is a 200-year anniversary. It had been 200 years since the United States declared its independence. The celebration, with many festivals and parades, continued all year long. The American people were especially proud because for 200 years they had proved that their way of government, the democratic way, could grow and change with the country. In some countries, people bring about change with guns and rifles. Americans are encouraged to bring about change through more peaceful methods. People can protest present policies or vote for officials who will represent their views.

**Jimmy Carter**

In 1976, Jimmy Carter from Georgia was elected as the thirty-ninth President of the United States. Throughout his term in office, President Carter wanted very much to bring peace to the world. He invited the heads of Egypt and Israel here to talk about peace. These discussions became known as the Camp David Accords. The President signed a treaty with Panama, which would turn over control of the Panama Canal to the country of Panama. He also tried to make friends with Cuba, a close neighbor, by sharing fishing waters with them. Later, he let over 125,000 Cubans come to the United States to make their homes here.

President Carter believed in human rights around the world. He was deeply troubled when the country of Iran held 52 Americans hostage for 444 days. The President was also very concerned when the Soviet Union sent its army into the country of Afghanistan. To show his anger at the Soviet Union, President Carter would not allow the athletes from the United States to go to the Soviet Union for the 1980 Summer Olympic Games.

On January 20 ,1981, Ronald Reagan became the fortieth President of the United States. It was also on that day that the American hostages in Iran were finally set free.

**Ronald Reagan**

After Ronald Reagan became President, problems persisted. The Soviet Union was still in Afghanistan, Egypt and Israel were still trying to agree on issues, and the economy was a problem at home. Inflation, which makes the cost of goods higher, and unemployment were making life very difficult for many Americans. President Reagan hoped to improve these problem areas during his term of office.

Sudden violence occurred at home. On March 30, 1981, a young man shot President Reagan. Reagan survived the assassination attempt. The 1980s saw more women seeking higher political offices. The 1984 presidential election was a historic one. In this election, Walter Mondale, the Democratic presidential nominee, chose Geraldine Ferraro to be his running mate. She was the first woman to become a major party's candidate for the office of Vice President. However, Mondale and Ferraro lost the election, and Ronald Reagan was elected to a second term. In his first term, Reagan had appointed Sandra Day O'Connor to the United States Supreme Court. O'Connor was the first woman to sit as a Supreme Court justice.

In 1988, George Bush was elected President. Many changes had been occurring throughout the world. In November, the Berlin Wall, a symbol of the Cold War, was torn down. In 1990, East and West Germany were reunified. In 1991, the Soviet Union collapsed.

**George Bush**

In August of 1990, Iraq invaded Kuwait in a dispute over oil prices and oil fields. To force Iraqi president Saddam Hussein to withdraw, President Bush gathered international support for a series of economic sanctions. In November 1990, the United Nations Security Council authorized the use of force if Iraq did not withdraw by January 15, 1991. When talks failed, Operation Desert Storm was launched. On February 27, Hussein agreed to a cease-fire, and Iraq withdrew from Kuwait.

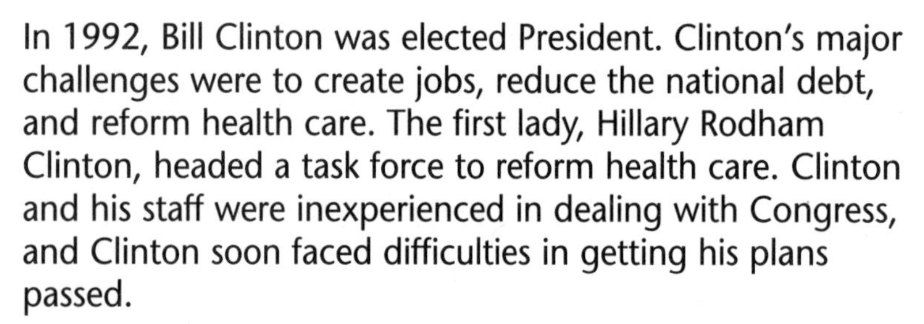

In 1992, Bill Clinton was elected President. Clinton's major challenges were to create jobs, reduce the national debt, and reform health care. The first lady, Hillary Rodham Clinton, headed a task force to reform health care. Clinton and his staff were inexperienced in dealing with Congress, and Clinton soon faced difficulties in getting his plans passed.

Meanwhile, foreign policy issues demanded his attention. While the President hoped to focus on domestic issues, he was soon forced to deal with problems in Haiti, Bosnia and Herzegovina, and the Middle East, and with trade concerns with Japan and China.

**Bill Clinton**

The last decades have seen many changes in the United States. The eight Presidents who served during these years have all left their mark upon America's history.

## What Did You Find Out?

**A** Match the United States President in column 1 with the event connected with him in column 2.

| | Column 1 | | Column 2 |
|---|---|---|---|
| ______ | 1. John F. Kennedy | a. | tried to reform health care. |
| ______ | 2. Lyndon B. Johnson | b. | was not elected to either the vice presidency or the presidency. |
| ______ | 3. Richard M. Nixon | c. | survived an assassination attempt. |
| ______ | 4. Gerald R. Ford | d. | worked on a program called the *Great Society.* |
| ______ | 5. Jimmy Carter | e. | sent troops to fight Saddam Hussein. |
| ______ | 6. Ronald Reagan | f. | was assassinated in Dallas, Texas. |
| ______ | 7. George Bush | g. | invited the heads of Egypt and Israel to Camp David. |
| ______ | 8. Bill Clinton | h. | was forced to resign after the Watergate scandal. |

**B** Write *True* or *False* on the line before each statement.

________________ 1. The United States celebrated its bicentennial on July 4, 1986.

________________ 2. President Johnson's programs to promote civil rights were called the *New Deal.*

________________ 3. President Nixon and his Vice President both resigned their offices.

________________ 4. President Kennedy completed two terms as President.

________________ 5. The Americans held hostage in Iran were released during President Ford's term of office.

________________ 6. President Nixon slowly brought home many of our soldiers from Vietnam.

**C** Complete each of the following statements. Write the correct name or date on the line provided.

1. In 1962, Russia agreed to stop building missile sites in ____________________.
2. John F. Kennedy was assassinated on this date: ____________________.
3. During ____________________ term, our government was sending many soldiers to Vietnam.
4. President ____________________ was invited to visit China.
5. ____________________ became the thirty-ninth President of the United States.
6. A country named ____________________ invaded Kuwait.

# Challenges for the United States



In its past, the United States had many problems to settle and many challenges to meet. This is still true today.

## The Economy

In Lesson 4 of Unit 4, you learned about the Great Depression. During that time, many people were jobless, lost their homes, or did not have enough money to buy food and clothing. Today, some people in our country are having these same problems. Both government and private organizations are working to provide basic necessities for all Americans.

## Energy

The United States is a land of machines. In Lesson 1 of Unit 4, you studied how machines changed life in this country. Today, we have more machines than ever before. Machines needed to produce goods require a source of energy to make them work. Electricity provides much of this energy. Electricity is often generated by the burning of fuels such as gas, oil, and coal. Hydroelectric power and nuclear energy are used to generate electricity, too. Cars, buses, trains, and airplanes need oil to run.

One result of these modern uses of fuels is that we are using up oil, gas, and coal at a very quick rate. Many of these fuels cannot be replaced very easily. Today, we must buy much of our fuel from other countries. Depending on other countries can be very costly. Hydroelectric plants use the power of falling water stored in reservoirs behind huge dams. Many people oppose the building of such dams because they destroy the natural environment. Nuclear fuels are abundant but can cause other problems. An accident involving nuclear fuels could cause great damage or loss of life. Our government has been trying to develop new sources and new types of fuel. All Americans can help by not wasting the fuels that they use.

## Hot Spots

Places in the world where countries are having problems are called *hot spots.* One of these places is the Middle East. The nation of Israel and the Arab countries around it have attacked each other. The United States has given Israel much economic, political, and military aid. However, at the same time, our nation has tried to help both Israel and the Arab countries solve their problems through peaceful means. These countries have fought many long wars. It is hoped that in the future, the people in these nations will find peaceful ways of resolving their differences.

## Foreign Policy

The way that the United States acts toward other countries is called our *foreign policy.* During part of our country's history, our foreign policy was to stay out of other countries' problems. For example, the United States was opposed to entering World War I when it first began. In Lesson 2 of this unit, you learned that our foreign policy was to help any country, such as Vietnam, that might be taken over by communism.

Today, the United States has several foreign policy goals. First, it wishes to work peacefully with countries throughout the world. Second, it wants to help nations that are our friends and that ask for aid. However, many Americans are not sure how much help should be given. The United States can choose to spend more money for foreign aid or for military needs. However, less money will then be available to spend in solving domestic problems. Our own country has many needs—for better education and improved cities, for example. Can we continue to provide foreign aid as we try to provide for our own domestic needs? Choices are difficult.

**Equal Rights**

Since the time of Thomas Jefferson, Americans have said that "all men are created equal." The history of our country, however, shows that not all Americans have been treated equally. In 1920, the Nineteenth Amendment to the Constitution granted the right to vote to all women. American Indians were not made citizens until June 15, 1924. Some religious as well as ethnic groups have also been treated unfairly. In earlier times, African Americans were enslaved and considered property. After they gained their freedom, many were not allowed to vote. They were not able to buy homes where they wished. They often had trouble getting a good education and good jobs.

One famous African-American civil rights leader was Dr. Martin Luther King, Jr. Dr. King, a minister by profession, led protests, boycotts, and marches throughout the country to gain fair treatment for all Americans. His "I Have a Dream" speech was given during a civil rights march in Washington, D.C. This speech inspired millions of Americans. Tragically, Dr. King was assassinated on April 4, 1968.

Through the efforts of King and many others, changes have been made. New civil rights laws were passed to provide more opportunities and equality for everyone. Although progress has been made, more must still be done to make our country truly equal for all Americans.

**Environment**

The United States has also had problems with its air and water. Because the country has long been industrialized, our land, air, and water have become polluted, or dirty. Waste materials have been dumped into our rivers and lakes. Automobiles have polluted the air. Factories have put smoke and harmful chemicals into our air and land. Laws have been passed to control pollution. There is a growing concern for the natural environment. As different areas are developed, including tropical rain forests, plant and animals species may be destroyed. People throughout the world are concerned about the loss of these species. At the same time, holes in the ozone layer of the atmosphere have been found and are increasing. The ozone layer protects animals from harmful rays of the sun. Many countries have agreed to stop using the chemicals that can cause the ozone layer to weaken and disappear. These are just a few of the environmental problems and concerns facing the United States and the world. Much needs to be done to protect the environment.

**Space Program**

On April 12, 1981, the first space shuttle, *Columbia,* was successfully launched into space. This launch was the beginning of a new space era. The United States seemed to be ready to meet new challenges.

Not all flights were successful. In January 1986, the space shuttle *Challenger* exploded shortly after takeoff. All seven astronauts on board were killed. One of these astronauts was a schoolteacher, Sharon Christa McAuliffe. She had hoped to teach children about life in space. The loss of the *Challenger* was a very sad day for all Americans and a major setback for the United States space program. Shuttles did not begin flying again until 1988. Since then, the space shuttle program has had much success. Astronauts have launched and repaired satellites, including the Hubble Space Telescope. Shuttles have docked with the Russian space station, and crew members have lived and worked alongside Russian cosmonauts. In 1996, astronaut Shannon Lucid spent almost six months in the space station—a record amount of time for an American astronaut in space.

**Famous Americans**

Like his father before him, this famous African American worked for equal freedoms and rights. He was a minister who believed that the differences between people should be solved in peaceable ways.

He was the leader of the Southern Christian Leadership Conference. This group did much to stop the unfair treatment of African Americans. As a leader of many civil rights marches and protests, he was put into jail and often treated very badly.

He won the 1964 Nobel Peace Prize for his efforts to gain equal rights and freedoms for all through peaceful means. He believed that laws could be changed without the use of force or weapons. Before he was killed by an assassin, this famous American gave a speech about making the United States better for all people. In this speech he said, "I have a dream . . ."

Who is this famous American? Write his name on the line under his picture.

______________________

## What Did You Find Out?

**A** Match the challenge in column 1 with its meaning in column 2.

| | Column 1 | Column 2 |
|---|---|---|
| ______ | 1. pollution | a. fair treatment for all Americans |
| ______ | 2. the economy | b. how the United States acts toward other countries |
| ______ | 3. equal rights | c. dirty air and water |
| ______ | 4. energy | d. places where countries are having problems |
| ______ | 5. hot spots | e. trade, jobs, business, and money |
| ______ | 6. foreign policy | f. fuel or other source of power |

**B** Answer the following questions. Use complete sentences.

1. What are two economic problems that affect some people in the United States today?
   a. ______________________________
   b. ______________________________
2. Why is the use of oil, gas, coal, and nuclear energy a problem today?
   ______________________________
3. What are two foreign policy goals of the United States today?
   a. ______________________________
   b. ______________________________
4. How did Dr. Martin Luther King, Jr., bring about change in civil rights laws?
   ______________________________
5. What is one example of pollution in our environment?
   ______________________________
6. This lesson has discussed challenges facing the United States.
   a. What do you think is the most important challenge facing the United States today?
   ______________________________
   b. Why do you think it is important? ______________________________
   ______________________________
   c. How would you meet this challenge? ______________________________
   ______________________________

R E V I E W

# Review Units 4–5

**A** The sentences below review the main ideas that you have studied in Units 4 and 5. Complete the sentences. Write your answers on the lines provided.

1. In the 1800s, inventors built new ____________________ to do work more easily and quickly.
2. Americans soon began buying things made in ____________________.
3. Small towns grew into crowded ____________________ because people moved to live near factories.
4. Poor, rundown parts of cities are called ____________________.
5. Factory workers joined together in groups called labor ____________________ to try to improve working conditions.
6. In 1867, the United States grew in size when it purchased ____________________ from Russia.
7. The ____________________ Islands became a territory in 1898 and a state in 1959.
8. The United States showed that it was becoming a world ____________________ when it took over many of Spain's islands after the Spanish-American War.
9. The ____________________ Canal was dug through a strip of land that joins North and South America.
10. The United States also sent explorers to both the ____________________ and ____________________ Poles.
11. In 1914, World War ____________________ began in Europe.
12. The countries in Europe were split into two groups: the Central Powers and the ____________________.
13. When the country of ____________________ did not stop sinking our ships, the United States entered the war.
14. The war ended on November 11, 1918, which is called ____________________.
15. President Roosevelt's plan to help end the depression was called the ____________________.
16. World War ____________________ began when Germany and Italy began taking over other countries.
17. The United States dropped ____________________ bombs on two Japanese cities.
18. After the war, the United States gave help called ____________________ to many countries in Europe.

REVIEW

19. The ________________________ was the line that divided Eastern Europe from Western Europe.

20. The Soviet Union and the Eastern European countries had ________________________ governments.

21. In the ________________________ War, Russia and the United States had an arms race but were not actually fighting.

22. The United States celebrated its 200th birthday, or ________________________, in 1976.

23. Richard Nixon resigned the presidency in 1974 to avoid possible ________________________ by the House of Representatives.

24. President Reagan appointed the first ________________________ as a Supreme Court justice during his first term in office.

25. The first ________________________ was successfully launched on April 12, 1981.

**B** You have learned about many people in America's history. Read the description of each person. Write the correct names on the lines provided.

1. I invented the telegraph. ______________________________________

2. I was a general who led American soldiers during World War I.

   ______________________________________

3. I was the President who asked countries to join the League of Nations.

   ______________________________________

4. I was the President who had a plan to help Americans during the Depression.

   ______________________________________

5. I was a dictator who led the Fascists in Italy. ______________________________________

6. I was a dictator who led the Nazis in Germany. ______________________________________

7. I commanded American soldiers in Europe and Africa during World War II.

   ______________________________________

8. I was in charge of American naval forces in the Pacific during World War II.

   ______________________________________

9. I was a President who was assassinated in Dallas, Texas, in 1963.

   ______________________________________

10. My major presidential program was called the *Great Society.*

   ______________________________________

REVIEW

11. I was the first President to visit China. ______________________

12. Americans were held hostage in Iran during my presidency.

______________________

13. The bicentennial celebration occurred during my presidency.

______________________

14. I was the fortieth President of the United States. ______________________

15. I was President during Operation Desert Storm. ______________________

16. I worked to improve civil rights. I was assassinated in 1968.

______________________

17. I had to deal with problems in Haiti and Bosnia.

______________________

**Presidents of the United States**

1 George Washington 1789–1797
2 John Adams 1797–1801
3 Thomas Jefferson 1801–1809
4 James Madison 1809–1817
5 James Monroe 1817–1825
6 John Quincy Adams 1825–1829
7 Andrew Jackson 1829–1837
8 Martin Van Buren 1837–1841
9 William Henry Harrison 1841
10 John Tyler 1841–1845
11 James Knox Polk 1845–1849
12 Zachary Taylor 1849–1850
13 Millard Fillmore 1850–1853
14 Franklin Pierce 1853–1857
15 James Buchanan 1857–1861
16 Abraham Lincoln 1861–1865
17 Andrew Johnson 1865–1869
18 Ulysses S. Grant 1869–1877
19 Rutherford B. Hayes 1877–1881
20 James Garfield 1881
21 Chester A. Arthur 1881–1885
22 Grover Cleveland 1885–1889
23 Benjamin Harrison 1889–1893
24 Grover Cleveland 1893–1897
25 William McKinley 1897–1901
26 Theodore Roosevelt 1901–1909
27 William Howard Taft 1909–1913
28 Woodrow Wilson 1913–1921
29 Warren G. Harding 1921–1923
30 Calvin Coolidge 1923–1929
31 Herbert Hoover 1929–1933
32 Franklin D. Roosevelt 1933–1945
33 Harry S Truman 1945–1953
34 Dwight D. Eisenhower 1953–1961
35 John F. Kennedy 1961–1963
36 Lyndon B. Johnson 1963–1969
37 Richard M. Nixon 1969–1974
38 Gerald R. Ford 1974–1977
39 James Earl Carter 1977–1981
40 Ronald W. Reagan 1981–1989
41 George H. W. Bush 1989–1993
42 William J. Clinton 1993–

# American History Time Line

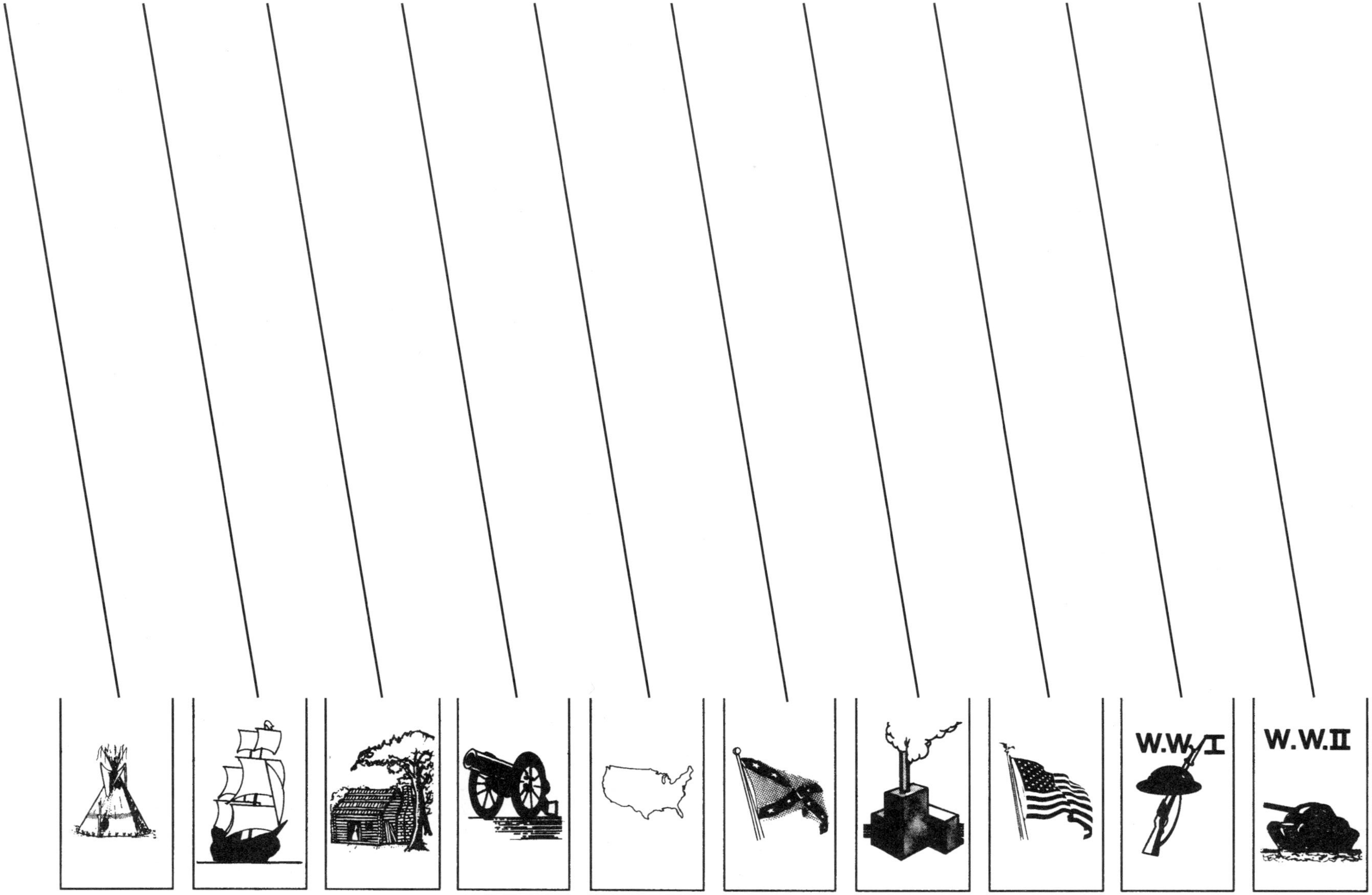

W.W.I

W.W.II

1 2 3 4 5 6 7 8 9 10

TEST

# End-of-Book Test

**A** Write *True* or *False* on the line before each statement.

_______________ **1.** The United States is on the continent of South America.

_______________ **2.** The Atlantic Ocean is off the east coast of the United States.

_______________ **3.** The first Americans probably came from Asia.

_______________ **4.** John Cabot sailed from Spain to explore parts of Canada.

_______________ **5.** Some settlers came to America because they wanted to worship as they pleased.

_______________ **6.** King Henry III was ruler of England during the Revolutionary War.

_______________ **7.** Thomas Jefferson wrote the Declaration of Independence.

_______________ **8.** The Constitution set up three branches of national government.

_______________ **9.** George Washington was the person who wrote most of the Constitution.

_______________ **10.** The first ten amendments to the constitution are called the *Bill of Rights.*

_______________ **11.** Few people decided to move west.

_______________ **12.** Robert E. Lee was the president of the Confederate States.

_______________ **13.** Machines helped farmers grow more crops.

_______________ **14.** The United States bought Alaska from Russia.

_______________ **15.** The Spanish-American War lasted for many years.

_______________ **16.** World War I started with an assassination in England.

_______________ **17.** Franklin D. Roosevelt suggested the New Deal as a way to get out of the Depression.

_______________ **18.** Germany, Italy, and Japan were on the same side in World War II.

_______________ **19.** The United States fought an unpopular war in Vietnam.

_______________ **20.** John Kennedy was assassinated by John Wilkes Booth.

_______________ **21.** The Iron Curtain separated Eastern and Western Europe.

_______________ **22.** The fall of the Berlin Wall was a symbol for the fall of communism.

_______________ **23.** The SALT talks were held to try to control the spread of nuclear weapons.

_______________ **24.** The Cold War is still going on between the United States and the Soviet Union.

_______________ **25.** Gerald Ford was the only President who was not elected as President or Vice President.

TEST

**B** Match the words in the first column with the meanings in the second column. Write the letter of the meaning on the line.

| |  | |  |
|---|---|---|---|
| ______ | 1. pollution | a. | a large body of water |
| ______ | 2. plantations | b. | land set aside for Indians to live on |
| ______ | 3. disarmament | c. | a long trip by water |
| ______ | 4. ocean | d. | large farms |
| ______ | 5. domestic problems | e. | a person who listens to both sides of a problem and then tries to decide what is fair for both sides |
| ______ | 6. reservation | f. | problems people face in their own country |
| ______ | 7. dictator | g. | taking apart or reducing existing arms or weapons |
| ______ | 8. voyage | h. | not taking one side or another |
| ______ | 9. arbitrator | i. | dirty air and water |
| ______ | 10. neutral | j. | a person who runs a country alone |

**C** Number the events in the correct order by writing the numbers 1 through 12 on the lines.

______ The United States Constitution was written.

______ The Civil War divided the country.

______ Only Indians lived in North America.

______ The colonies fought a war with England and won their freedom.

______ The Cold War ended with the dismantling of the Soviet Union.

______ Europeans explore the Americas.

______ The United States helped defeat the Axis during World War II.

______ The Louisiana Purchase doubled the size of the United States.

______ Settlers came to America looking for a better life.

______ Bill Clinton was elected President.

______ The Great Depression put many people out of work.

______ The United States joined the Allies during World War I.

TEST

**D** Underline the word or phrase that best completes each of the following sentences.

1. The name given to boats used by some Indians was (whalers, canoes, square-riggers).
2. Magellan's ship sailed (to Newfoundland, to America, around the world).
3. Members of the Continental Congress were called (delegates, settlers, soldiers).
4. Thomas Jefferson wrote the (Constitution, Declaration of Independence, Declaration of Rights).
5. James Polk believed that our country should stretch from (the North to the South, the Atlantic to the Pacific, Mississippi to Missouri).
6. Settlers were given free land under the (California Act, Nebraska Act, Homestead Act).
7. The North and South were divided over the issue of (trade, slavery, war).
8. The battleship *Maine* was blown up in the harbor at Havana, (Illinois, Egypt, Cuba).
9. World War I was fought mostly on the continent of (Asia, Africa, Europe).
10. Atomic bombs were dropped on Hiroshima and (Nagasaki, Tokyo, Guam).

**E** Write the name of the President described in each sentence.

| | | | |
|---|---|---|---|
| John Kennedy | Richard Nixon | Jimmy Carter | George Bush |
| Lyndon Johnson | Gerald Ford | Ronald Reagan | Bill Clinton |

____________________ 1. This President suggested programs to help poor people and called it the *Great Society.*

____________________ 2. He was President during the bicentennial.

____________________ 3. This President sent United States troops to fight Saddam Hussein.

____________________ 4. This President worked with Israel and Egypt on a peace treaty.

____________________ 5. This President had to deal with problems in Haiti and Bosnia.

____________________ 6. This President visited China.

____________________ 7. This President faced the Cuban missile crisis.

____________________ 8. This President took office on the same day that American hostages were freed from Iran.